It's another Quality Book from CGP

This book is for anyone doing GCSE English or English Literature.

It contains lots of tricky questions designed
to make you sweat — because that's the only
way you'll get any better.

It's also got some daft bits in to try and make
the whole experience at least vaguely
entertaining for you.

What CGP is all about

Our sole aim here at CGP is to produce the highest quality
books — carefully written, immaculately presented and
dangerously close to being funny.

Then we work our socks off to get them out to you
— at the cheapest possible prices.

CONTENTS

Section Five — Original Writing

Section Six — Media and Non-Fiction Questions

Section Seven — Language

Published by Coordination Group Publications Ltd.

Editors:
Taissa Csáky
James Paul Wallis

Contributors:
Elspeth Bain
Shona McIntosh
Victoria Morgan

ISBN: 978 1 84146 288 2

Groovy website: www.cgpbooks.co.uk
Jolly bits of clipart from CorelDRAW®
Printed by Elanders Hindson Ltd, Newcastle upon Tyne.

Planning & Introductions

Q1 Turn the points below into an essay plan by sorting them out under the headings **Introduction**, **Middle** and **Conclusion**.

- Too much 'leisure' time spent sitting behind computers or watching TV and videos — too little exercise = increased risk of heart disease, and constant use of electricity causing pollution.

  Spend less time watching TV/using computers — do a bit more exercise for fun.

- Need to change the way we live.

- <u>Is</u> possible to change the way we live by choosing more carefully what we eat, and by being more active. This will make our lifestyles much healthier, and be far better for the environment.

- Driving cars — not enough exercise, using up the world's oil and creating pollution.

  Can use public transport, or even better cycle or walk to work or shops.

- Way we live not just unhealthy for us — not good for the environment either.

- Busy work schedules mean less time to prepare proper food.

  Convenience foods don't have enough nutrients in them for a healthy balanced diet. Also convenience foods have more packaging — creates more rubbish.

  We can take time to prepare fresh food — healthier diet and less rubbish.

Q2 This introduction rambles on without making a clear point.
Write it out again and underline everything that shouldn't be in an introduction.

> Modern lifestyles are becoming more unhealthy, and this is something which my Mum has been saying for ages. When I was in the shower last week, she said that I had been wasting loads of hot water. There is an increased risk of heart disease due to lack of exercise, and general ill health caused by poor eating habits. We can choose to walk or cycle to the shops or to work, instead of using up the world's natural resources. Increasingly, the way we live our daily lives needs to change, if we are to stop the damage we are doing to ourselves and the world around us.

Q3 Use your essay plan from Q1 to write a brief paragraph for a) – c).
Make sure you stick to the point.

a) An introduction, briefly describing what the essay is about.

b) One paragraph from the middle part of the essay.

c) A conclusion summarizing all the main points with a general statement to conclude the essay.

Formal and Informal Language

Q1   Rewrite these paragraphs in formal essay-style English.

a) *I reckon Shakespeare makes Oberon and Titania have a go at each other because he wants to point out the difference between people who just get things sorted and know the score, and people who just run about falling in and out of love all of the time.*

b) By writing about that Willy Loman bloke, Arthur Miller makes us think about the way we treat every Joe Bloggs in the street. I feel well sorry for him.

c) *All that snow and white stuff makes you think of winter. I think the weather shows how the poet is feeling as well, because she must be lonely and bored being indoors all the time. This first bit of the poem sort of makes you think this for the rest of the poem, too.*

d) Shakespeare is having a go at us for fancying people just because of what they look like. We can see this when he makes Demitrius dump Helena the first time around because he thinks she's really ugly.

Q2   You don't always have to write in formal language. Sometimes you're tested on how well you can write in other styles. Rewrite the paragraph below in tabloid newspaper style.

> Scientists have long believed that many of the cures to modern diseases are to be found under the sea bed, and recent studies in the pharmaceutical industry have suggested that there could also be a marine-based substance that can radically alter the signs of aging. The chemical, which is present in a rare type of coral, is said to improve the elasticity of the epidermis by 98 per cent when taken internally in tablet form. This new study has produced an uproar in environmentalist circles, who claim that the financial profit which the pharmaceutical industry stands to gain from this finding poses a serious threat to the coral which they say is a protected species.

Q3   In original writing you have to use your own style. The sentences below are all in formal language. Rewrite them so they evoke different moods and feelings.

a)   The midday sun shone down on the water, casting reflections on the boats and people moving about.

b)   The gothic-style building stood upon the steep hill, surrounded by many trees and various shrubs of a thorny variety.

c)   The large brown horse finished the race, then walked around at a slow pace sweating.

d)   The five hungry children saw the dinner table full of a large variety of different foods.

Giving Evidence & Quoting

Q1   Write out the paragraphs below, then underline the evidence backing up the statement alongside.

a) After running about in the garden all day, Felix finally came indoors to eat his food. When Katy bent down to pat him, she noticed pieces of red cloth sticking out from between his teeth which matched the colour of Pete's slippers. Felix ate all of his food happily.

Felix chewed Pete's slippers.

b) Patricia looked fantastic as she pulled up in her shiny new sports car. It was a beautiful day, and her neighbour Daniel was outside doing some gardening when she emerged from the car, shouting over to him, 'Hey, Dan, what do you think of my new car?' At that moment, Daniel turned on his lawn mower and pretended not to have heard her.

Daniel was jealous of Patricia's new car.

c) The wind was blowing hard and Skipper Johnson had a bad feeling in his stomach. The colour of the sky didn't look good to him. He knew he had to tell the others that it might come to the point of abandoning ship within an hour, as he watched the waves crashing over the deck.

Skipper Johnson knew there was danger ahead.

Q2   Write out the sentences below, putting in quotation marks where you think there is a direct quote.

a) Mrs.Wittaker said, If I don't get the children vaccinated, I could be putting their lives in danger. There are plenty of parents like Mrs.Wittaker who feel the same way. (Mrs.M.Wittaker, The News Today, 2002)

b) There can be no excuses for children who do not get their homework in on time. I am prepared to stay behind after school to supervise detentions. Mr. Snodgrass, the chemistry teacher, had to make this clear after receiving only four homework books last Tuesday. (Mr.P.W.Snodgrass, Schools in Focus Weekly, 2002)

Q3   Now rewrite the sentences from Q2 in such a way that you don't need speech marks.

Make sure you don't change the meaning of the original.

Q4   The paragraphs below don't make much sense — the quotes are in the wrong place. Rewrite the paragraphs, rearranging the sentences so the quotes make more sense.

a) *"We're getting better after each game," the team's manager said yesterday. There have been frequent criticisms of the country's leading football team recently, despite the fact that they are still at the top of the premier division. However, other pundits have put the recent wave of criticism down to jealousy of the team's success, and point out that it has certainly not altered their performance at all. This comes after a remark made by a major sports journalist who described them on prime time television as being "dirty players with no real tactics."*

b) *When asked how she felt about having such a flower named after her, Suzie Starlet gushed simply, "I'm flattered and honoured." A flower show spokesperson described the now famous flower as "a beautiful pink and orange rose with a delicate perfume." A new flower has been named after the glamorous film actress, Suzie Starlet. The flower, now to be known as a 'Pink Suzie' was unveiled yesterday by its famous namesake at the annual flower show in Brighton.*

Writing in Paragraphs

Q1 There are five good reasons for changing paragraph in the box.
Write down the reason for the paragraph change in each of these pieces of writing.

> *new person   new time   new place   new person speaking   new topic*

a)   The rain poured down onto the busy street as Mr. Sanders picked his way through noisy street-sellers, filthy children and stray dogs. The whole city seemed intent on keeping him from his appointment.

At High Court House, Miss Loxham was impatiently awaiting the arrival of her tutor.

b)   "If we hide in the hedge he'll never find us," hissed Susan, as they sprinted across the field, away from the old man's house.

"But I don't think we can make it before he sees us," replied Danny, between breaths. He gave her a frightened look and they increased their pace, adrenaline flowing through their veins.

c)   Osteo-arthritis is now easily treated by the hip replacement operation. This operation is a great success story for medical science. Although quite a complicated procedure, there's an almost 100% success rate in patients.

However, rheumatoid arthritis is far less easy to treat. As yet, there is no known method of ridding patients of the disease, although it can be controlled by drugs.

d)   Mrs Jain commented that the play was a triumph. The actors were excellent and the performance and comedy timing were extremely slick.

Miss Booth, on the other hand, felt that the casting of 'Roxy' was unwise, as she tended to dominate the stage and stifle the other characters' performances.

Q2 Split each piece of writing into sensible paragraphs.

a) Two years ago this building was derelict, awaiting demolition. Luckily, two businessmen saw it and noticed its potential. They decided to buy it, despite many people thinking they were mad to take such a risk. Now, it houses a thriving restaurant, popular with A-list celebrities and it is impossible to get a table unless you know the maître d'.

b) Sarah was sitting in the common room, singing to herself and reading a trashy magazine. She was waiting for Gareth to pick her up and he was always late so she'd come prepared. The door creaked and Paul came into the room, looking embarrassed. He had something to tell her and she wasn't going to like it.

c) "I'm afraid I'm sacking you, Pete," said Mr. Rogers sternly. "But it was an accident Mr. Rogers — I swear. If I'd known I was going to set fire to the building I'd never have started smoking in the first place," cried Pete. He gave Mr. Rogers his most pleading, innocent look, but it was too late. "I'm sorry, son, but this time you went too far."

Q3 Write two paragraphs on your favourite sport. Make sure there's a change of topic in the second one.

Writing in Paragraphs

Q1 These paragraphs sound very disjointed. Use linking words to make them flow more smoothly. Reword the first sentence of each paragraph if it will help you.

a)   I couldn't understand what had possessed Arthur to paint his living room lime green. It looked horrendous and it took all my powers of pretence to congratulate him on the new look.

        There's no accounting for taste and perhaps in five years' time it will be the height of fashion and everyone will have lime green walls.

b)   In the present day we crave material goods above everything else. You only need to look at the millions of people across the country who enter the lottery each week, hoping to boost their spending powers.

        People are working longer hours and taking less holiday. It's not healthy and it's becoming clear that we need to readdress our priorities in life.

c)   Mountain-climbing is a potentially dangerous sport. Every year people die in their pursuit of reaching the summit, but this doesn't put others off.

        It is necessary to prepare carefully for a mountain expedition. You need to take lots of different equipment to cover a large number of eventualities.

Q2 These paragraphs are in a terrible order. Reorder them so they're clear and logical.

a)   "We understand a substantial proportion of the new notes are still in bank or Post Office branches and have not been issued to the general public," said a Bank of England spokesman.

        The Bank of England has made an embarrassing discovery. It has had to halt distribution of the new £5 note after it was discovered parts of the note's design were disappearing.

        The Bank stated that about 10 million of the new £5 notes had been distributed. The new note is the same size and colour as the old fiver.

b)   Increased emissions of methane are also contributing to the greenhouse effect, although on a far smaller scale than carbon dioxide. One reason for the increased emissions is the modern practice of intensive animal farming.

        The most significant factor contributing to global warming is increased emissions of carbon dioxide, the main greenhouse gas. Extensive deforestation and fossil-fuel burning are leading to high levels of carbon dioxide in the air.

Q3 Write a separate paragraph for each bullet point.

a)
- We eat too much junk food
- We don't take enough exercise
- On average people are getting fatter and unhealthier
- Need to change lifestyle

b)
- Selina arrived at her new school
- No one spoke to her all morning
- Jo started chatting to Selina at lunchtime 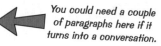 _You could need a couple of paragraphs here if it turns into a conversation._
- She felt much happier

Writing Conclusions

Q1   Rearrange these sentences so they form a conclusion to the question below.

*Does anything actually happen in the play to change
the way we perceive the plight of its main characters?*

a)   The writer creates a perpetual cycle of anticipation and boredom throughout the play which comes to represent the human condition.

b)   The mere promise of change gives the play momentum, but the plight of the main characters does not change, nor does our perception of it.

c)   Estragon and Vladimir have episodes of activity throughout the play, and there are moments when it seems as though something will happen, or that the scene will change dramatically.

d)   There can be no dispute that at the end of the play, we are left with the feeling that nothing significant has really changed.

Q2   Copy out the conclusion below. Underline any mistakes or bits that shouldn't be in a conclusion.

> I couldn't really make my mind up at first, but I think that at the end of the play, we are left with the feeling that nothing significant has really changed. I found the play very boring. Estragon and Vladimir have episodes of activity throughout the play, and there are moments when it seems as though something will happen, or that the scene will change dramatically. In Act Two it looks as if something exciting might happen, but then the characters just go back to talking about Godot. The mere promise of change gives the play momentum, but the plight of the main characters does not change, nor does our perception of it. The writer creates a perpetual cycle of anticipation and boredom throughout the play which comes to represent the human condition.

Q3   Using the information in the box, write a conclusion which answers the question below, summarises what you think, and makes a final statement.

What is the main difference between people who dance and those who don't?

- There seems to be a great division between people who like to dance and those who don't.

- The ability to really let yourself go on the dance floor comes down to a question of confidence. Those who don't have any difficulty dancing wildly in front of others always seem to be the centre of attention in other areas of their lives. Those who seem to lack confidence in general, tend to lurk in the shadows at discos, pretending not to want to dance, when really they do.

- Confidence is not something we are simply born with, it can also be learned. A recent study carried out in California showed that 8 people in every 10 who were questioned regarded themselves as 'not that confident really,' but when asked to perform circus tricks in front of a live audience, they were all successful in completing the task. So the main division between those who dance and those who don't seems to be a matter of choice as much as anything.

Essays, schmessays — I'd like to see the examiners write some...

Conclusions are easy to muck up in an exam — especially when you don't leave enough time to write one. So keep half an eye on that clock all the way through.

Answering Literature Questions

Q1 Read the question below, and the points I've written down to help me write an answer. Decide which of the points are **not** good points to include in the answer, and write them down.

> Question: What do we learn about equality in Animal Farm, and how does Orwell achieve this?

> _Points for my answer:_
>
> * _Examples of inequality amongst the animals._
>
> * _How Orwell shows the difference between the way the animals treat each other when they have no power and when some of them do._
>
> * _The way George Orwell was brought up._
>
> * _Examples of apparent harmony amongst the animals._
>
> * _Different types of farming methods._
>
> * _The ideas about equality we are left with at the end of the book._
>
> * _One of the main characters._

Q2 Write down what type of question you think each of the below are — whether they're asking about: the **writer's message**; the **characters**; or are about **different cultures and traditions**.

a) In **The Merchant of Venice**, the female characters appear to possess more knowledge and wisdom than the male ones. How does Shakespeare achieve this?

b) Compare the attitudes and feelings of the main characters in **I Know Why the Caged Bird Sings** and **The Bell Jar**. What are the main differences and similarities between the two cultures in which they are set?

c) Compare some of the themes explored in **Of Mice and Men** and **The Pearl**. What do you think Steinbeck's attitude towards his own culture is, and how is this conveyed?

d) **The Ministry of Fear** is a poem which places particular emphasis on the act of naming. What do you think Heaney is trying to convey about personal and political identity?

Q3 Using the familiar story of **The Three Little Pigs** as a guide, create a brief essay plan which would help to answer the question below:

> Question: How does the behaviour of the third pig in **The Three Little Pigs** differ from pig number one and pig number two, and how does this result in the wolf's eventual defeat?

___Writing About Characters___

Q1   Read the paragraphs below about characters, and write down which character assessment suits them best.

a) | *Jane ran into the school yard with a sudden burst of energy like a gust of wind. Her excited laughter could be heard from the car park as she quickly flung her bag to the floor, grabbed her friend Sophie and twirled them both around and around in a dizzying spin.*

Jane is:

   i)   A lazy, unfriendly, and boring girl who doesn't like playing outdoors.

   ii) A young, excitable school girl with lots of energy, who likes to have fun with friends.

   iii) A tired, sad old lady who can't walk very far.

b) | *Mrs.Wilkes saw from the corner of the door that Mr.Wilkes was sleeping. His fluffy, white hair seemed to cradle his chubby, smiling face like a bonnet, as he slowly inhaled and exhaled the late afternoon air. She chuckled to herself quietly, before closing the door and heading back out into the garden.*

Mr.Wilkes is:

   i)   A restless, fierce man who everyone is afraid of, including his wife.

   ii) A highly strung, arrogant male model with chiselled cheek bones and an athletic physique.

   iii) A peaceful, elderly, but child-like man, who's happy to let his wife mother him.

Q2   Write out the speech below and <u>underline</u> the parts which you think show what type of character Puck is. Then write at least two sentences describing what you think Puck is like.

> PUCK: Captain of our fairy band,
>   Helena is here at hand,
>   And the youth, mistook by me,
>   Pleading for a lover's fee,
>   Shall we their fond pageant see?
>   Lord, what fools these mortals be!
>
> OBERON: Stand aside: the noise they make
>   Will cause Demitrius to awake.
>
> PUCK: Then will two at once woo one;
>   That must needs be sport alone;
>   And those things do best please me
>   That befall prepost'rously.
>
> Act III, Scene II, *A Midsummer Night's Dream*

Q3   Mr.Wilkes from Q1 has been murdered. There are three suspects. Write a short speech for each suspect making sure that what they say makes them come across as very different characters.

   a)   Make A sound like he was after Mr. Wilkes's money.

   b)   Make B sound like he was jealous.

   c)   Make C sound like she was angry with Mr. Wilkes.

Writing About Characters

Q1   For each paragraph below, write a short sentence describing what the main characters are like.

a)   The Wicked Queen of Avalonia knew that she was doomed to a fate of certain execution within the coming days, for a crime she did not commit. She had nothing left to lose, and was now free to seek revenge for the many years of ill treatment she had suffered at the hands of her cruel chiropodist. However, she thought it best to keep quiet about it all, not wanting to upset everyone.

b)   Mr.Finchley just hadn't been the same after winning the lottery three years ago. His neighbours soon noticed that he'd stopped going to the local pub on a Friday night, and, apart from the six foot high electric fencing around his house, everybody seemed to wonder what he spent all his money on. People began to call him greedy and snobby. Then one day in June, the word got around that he had died suddenly, leaving all of his fortune to John the milkman.

c)   Lovely Mrs.Tabble was a kind old dinner lady, who took good care of the children at Saint Judith's, and always brought special sweets for them on Fridays. Katie, a girl from school, was very surprised and saddened to see Mrs.Tabble angrily kicking her dog in the park, one afternoon in the summer holidays.

Q2   Quoting from the paragraphs in Q1, write a few short sentences to answer the questions below:

a) | How can we tell that the Wicked Queen of Avalonia isn't really wicked? |

b) | What makes us distrust the neighbours' opinion of Mr.Finchley? |

c) | How does Katie's reaction to Mrs.Tabble affect our view of her? |

Q3   Briefly rewrite the three stories outlined in Q1 from the point of view of each of the main characters.

Q4   Which of the characters below from Q1 a) are the most **reliable** source on the Wicked Queen of Avalonia's character? Write down the reasons for your answer.

a)   Wicked Queen of Avalonia: "I am very afraid of dying, but I know that I am innocent of the charge I have been branded with. I have been set up."

b)   Cruel Chiropodist: "She was a mean old girl, who never thought twice about kicking me whilst I tried to do her feet. It doesn't surprise me that she's a thief as well."

c)   Baker of Avalonia: "I saw her steal some bread out of my shop, and she definitely deserves to die."

The Writer's Message

Q1   Choosing from the questions below, write down the ones which you think are **message questions**.

a)   *"How do we get to know the character of Puck in **A Midsummer Night's Dream**?"*

b)   *"What do you think Shakespeare is saying about love in **Romeo and Juliet**?"*

c)   *"What methods does Larkin employ to describe the world of work in **Toads Revisited**?"*

d)   *"What does **Educating Rita** tell us about the way society operates?"*

Q2   Write out the points below, dividing them into four lists, headed: **Story**, **Characters**, **Tone** and **Title**.

> * Conrad uses the other characters mainly to symbolise different aspects of African and Western culture.
>
> * 'Heart of Darkness' is a very negative title, and it suggests Conrad's ultimately pessimistic view of human existence and human nature.
>
> * One of sadness, anger, and a lack of optimism for the future.
>
> * Marlow goes on a journey up the Congo River, where he eventually meets Mr. Kurtz, and experiences first hand the corruption of the wilderness and its people.
>
> * Main characters are Marlow, who is travelling on behalf of a Belgian trading company, and Mr. Kurtz, an ivory trader who holds a position of power over the inhabitants of the area and is described in negative terms.
>
> * Conrad is scathing about Marlow's life in England.
>
> * Ideas of corruption are explored on many levels throughout Marlow's narrative.

Q3   Using the brief overview you created in Q2 as a guide, write down which of these sentences you think best describes the writer's message in **Heart of Darkness**.

a)   It's wrong to trade in ivory, and Mr. Kurtz is the culprit for the world's corruption.

b)   The heart of human existence is always susceptible to 'darkness' and corruption, and colonialism is an example of this.

c)   Don't travel up the Congo River without telling someone where you're going.

d)   Marlow's narration of the story is influenced by Mr. Kurtz, and therefore isn't that reliable.

Q4   Answer these questions about **Goldilocks and the Three Bears**.

a)   Using the story **Goldilocks and the Three Bears** as your text, create a brief overview like the one in Q2, with the headings: Story, Characters, tone and title.

b)   Using your overview, write a brief sentence describing what you think the writer's message is in **Goldilocks and the Three Bears**.

Different Cultures and Traditions

Q1   Write out the words below. Circle those which are unfamiliar to you and underline the words which are spelt so they sound like an accent or dialect.

shrine	cumdach	everyting	everything
important	bigibigi	laidak	rogue
chifforobe	cabinet	this morning	dis marnin'

Q2   Write down everything from this extract that tells you it is from a different culture.

> This is how I make a living.
>
> During the week I work at the Institute teaching English to people who want to live elsewhere. At the weekend I buy and sell cars.
>
> Viktor can see the harbour from his building, so he comes over and tells me when there's a Japanese ship in port. I go down to the harbour and talk to the sailors, then we go and sit in a cafe and have a drink. Usually it turns out they have a car to sell because they know they can get a good price here. So I take the car off their hands.
>
> The Japanese cars are left-hand drive, but that doesn't bother my customers. Most of them are stupid country muzhiks who don't know what side of the road they should be driving anyway.
>
> When I've paid the sailor and given Viktor his bottle of vodka and paid off the harbour master and paid my dues to the mafia, I can finally take the car out to the villages.
>
> In summer it's hell because the roads are so dusty; in winter it's hell because of the snow and ice; and in spring and autumn the roads are a sea of mud. Maybe winter's the best because at least the cars don't get so dirty.

[What a bargain.]

Q3   Write two or three sentences about the extract in Q2 to answer the question below. Don't forget quotes to back up what you say.

> **How does the writer show that the narrator feels dissatisfied with his way of life?**

The Writer's Techniques

Q1   Rewrite the paragraph below in the style of: a) **a spooky murder mystery**; b) **a romantic love story**; c) **a news report**.

> *Julia sat by the fire and kept warm. She knew that Martin, the boy from the village, had said he would be there at eight o'clock to take her out. It was now eight thirty, and Julia looked over to the window to see if she could spot his car, but it was raining, and there was no sign of him.*

Q2   Answer these questions about Ms. Simmonds.

     a)   Using the information below, write down which type of character you think Ms.Simmonds is.

> Ms. Simmonds: *"I am very pleased you are able to come to my party. It will start promptly at seven thirty. Please dress according to the standards I have indicated on the invitation. One bottle of medium-priced wine will suffice as a gift."*

         i)   A very organised woman who knows what she wants.
         ii)   A bumbling idiot, who can't string two sentences together.
         iii)   A very funny woman, who has everybody in stitches.

     b)   Choosing from the list below, write down the styles used to create the character of Ms.Simmonds.

         i)   Short, simple sentences.
         ii)   Lots of fancy comparisons.
         iii)   Unusual, difficult words.
         iv)   Formal wording.
         v)   No fancy comparisons.

Q3   Answer these questions about the paragraph below.

     a)   Copy out the paragraph below, and <u>underline</u> the bits that you feel help to set the scene.

> *Julia sat in the lonely old vicarage, huddling in close to the fire, trying to keep warm. The huge stone walls were damp and gave off a mouldy stench. Trying not to move, she forced herself to turn and face the cobweb covered windows, which looked out onto the darkness of the windswept causeway.*

     b)   Now write a couple of sentences to say how this is supposed to make us feel.

Q4   Write a brief paragraph which **foreshadows** the disappearance of Martin in Q1.

Useful Literature Words

Q1 Write out the sentences below and place them under their correct heading of **simile** or **metaphor**.

* My boss is an immature little baby.
* Mark's father was as nice as pie when he came home.
* The sea was like a pane of glass.
* The people of the world are tenants and God is the landlord.
* The plane soared effortlessly as a bird into the blue sky.
* Jason's new bike was the Rolls Royce of mountain bikes.
* The Moon is the mother of the planets.
* The woman in the pub was howling like a banshee.

Q2 Choosing from the list below, write down which idea or emotion you think the imagery of the horses symbolises in this sentence:

Sarah leaned on her crutches as she watched the horses bolt away from the starting line with ease and vigour.

i) You shouldn't break your leg if you like watching horses.

ii) Sarah's love of horses.

iii) Sarah's desire to be able to walk again.

Q3 The story below is an allegory about Mr. Jones, his children, and a jealous neighbour, Mr. Hamilton. Rewrite the allegory, turning it back into a straightforward story about Mr. Jones and Mr. Hamilton.

Shepherd Jones loved his sheep. He worked hard in the hills all day, to make sure that his sheep were all safe and well fed. One day he decided to build a huge sheep pen for them, so that he would know where they all were.

A jealous farmer, Mr. Huffy, didn't like the fact that Shepherd Jones had so many healthy sheep, and had built such a huge sheep pen, so one night he went out into the hills and knocked down all the walls of the pen, leaving the sheep to scatter across the hills. The next day, Shepherd Jones was distraught at the sight of his broken sheep pen, and that none of his sheep were to be found. He knew he would have to start the sheep farm up again from nothing.

Q4 Write a few sentences explaining why John's liking for the food in the sentence below is **ambiguous**.

John couldn't eat another thing at Madge's dinner party. He was very interested to know what ingredients she had been using.

Q5 Write out the sentences below and underline the **ironic** bits.

Christopher had always been a brainy grade A student. So everybody had really expected him to fail disastrously at the children's spelling competition.

Sally was her usual inconspicuous self, with a bright pink and purple t-shirt and yellow striped jeans.

Reading Plays

Q1 Read the plot outlines, then write down which of these Shakespeare plays is a **tragedy**, which one's a **comedy**, and which one's a **history**.

> **King Lear** — Lear, a mythical king, hands England over to his two selfish and power-hungry daughters. He ends up mad and homeless, but learns that love is more important than power or position.

> **Twelfth Night** — A young woman called Viola dresses up as a man. A woman called Olivia falls in love with Viola in her new outfit and Viola falls in love with her boss, Orsino...meanwhile the other characters are always drunk or fighting...they all live happily ever after.

> **King Henry V** — based on the story of the real Henry V. Henry goes to France with an English army where he fights a battle at Agincourt, and wins a massive victory.

Q2 Read the passages below from Much Ado About Nothing, and write down which is: a) a **monologue** b) a **dialogue** c) an **aside** d) a **soliloquy**.

i)
> WATCH: _(aside)_ I know that Deformed; a' has been a vile thief this seven years; a' goes up and down like a gentleman: I remember his name.

Act III, Scene III

HINT: _The Friar's explaining a plan, so he's probably talking to someone._

ii)
> FRIAR: Marry, this well carried, shall on her behalf
> Change slander to remorse; that is some good:
> But not for that dream I on this strange course,
> But on this travail look for greater birth.
> She dying, as it must be so maintain'd,
> Upon the instant that she was accus'd,
> Shall be lamented, pitied and excus'd
> Of every hearer; for it so falls out
> That what we have we prize not to the worth
> Whiles we enjoy it.....

Act IV, Scene I

iii)
> BENEDICK: I do much wonder that one man, seeing how much another man is a fool when he dedicates his behaviours to love, will, after he hath laughed at such shallow follies in others, become the argument of his own scorn by falling in love: and such a man is Claudio... He was wont to speak plain and to the purpose, like an honest man and a soldier; and now he is turned orthographer; his words are a very fantastical banquet, just so many strange dishes. May I be so converted, and see with these eyes?

Act II, Scene III

HINT: _Benedick's talking about fairly personal stuff, so he's probably talking to himself._

iv)
> BENEDICK: Lady Beatrice, have you wept all this while?
>
> BEATRICE: Yea, and I will weep a while longer.
>
> BENEDICK: I will not desire that.
>
> BEATRICE: You have no reason; I do it freely.

Act IV, Scene I

Q3 Write out the passage from Q2 iv), and include brief details of the stage design, any action that takes place, and put in brackets how the characters are speaking. Aim to create a very sad, depressing scene.

Words To Use When You're Writing About Poetry

Q1 Write out the sentences below and underline the words that you think are used for either their **assonance**, **alliteration** or **onomatopoeia**. Write down assonance, alliteration or onomatopoeia after each sentence.

a) Cute Carly loved the cuddly clown she got for Christmas.

b) Sheila leaped across the heath to where the sheep were fast asleep.

c) The snake hissed at the guide as he tried to hush the noisy children behind him.

d) Rachel ran across the reading room with a thud, as the buzzing bees chased her.

Q2 Poets include pauses, or break up the lines of poetry in a particular way to add style, and to draw emphasis to certain words. Write down each name for the types of methods being used in the examples below.

a) | Thom had a talent for backing great losers at every meeting they went to.

b) | *The sword was drawn: her fate was cast*
The knight fell back, the moment passed.

c) | She saw the shadows creeping down the stairs so softly, passing her by.

Q3 Write down whether the lines below are in a regular rhythm or irregular rhythm.

a) *The baker knew the flour had not been bought.*

b) *But baking bread was something he did exceptionally well.*

Q4 The syntax of a poem means the order in which the words are written. Rewrite the lines below, using the same words but in a different order, to alter their meaning.

a) *The loud man was waving and grimacing.*

b) *The old lady was well-dressed but poor.*

Q5 Poets can change the pace of a poem by using words that make it sound either quick, slow, clunky or graceful. Add or remove words from the clunky line below, to make it sound: a) **quick**; b) **slow**; c) **graceful**.

Glenda knew it was time to go when the traffic light went green.

Q6 The tone of a poem is created when words are chosen to evoke certain feelings, such as anger, happiness, or regret. Rewrite the line in Q3 a), and add words which create a tone of: a) **anger**; b) **happiness**; c) **fear**.

Comparing

Q1 The two poems below share the same main subject matter. Read them both through and then choose from the list below, what you think the main subject of each poem is: a) **Mermaids**, b) **The sea**, c) **Walking your dog**, or d) **Singing**.

1 It keeps eternal whisperings around

 Desolate shores, and with its mighty swell

 Gluts twice ten thousand Caverns, till the spell

 Of Hecate* leaves them their old shadowy sound.   *Greek Goddess

5 Often 'tis in such gentle temper found,

 That scarcely will the very smallest shell

 Be moved for days from where it sometime fell,

 When last the winds of Heaven were unbound.

 Oh ye! who have your eyeballs vexed and tired,

10 Feast them upon the wideness of the Sea;

 Oh ye! whose ears are dinned with uproar rude,

 Or fed too much with cloying melody -

 Sit ye near some old Cavern's Mouth and brood,

 Until ye start, as if the sea nymphs quired*!   *choired

On the Sea, John Keats, 1817

---

1 *I started Early - Took my Dog -*

 And visited the Sea -

 The Mermaids in the Basement

 Came out to look at me -

2 *And Frigates* - in the Upper Floor*   *warships

 Extended Hempen Hands -*   *rope

 Presuming Me to be a Mouse -

 Aground - upon the Sands -

3 *But no Man moved Me - till the Tide*

 Went past my simple Shoe -

 And past my Apron - and my Belt

 And past my Bodice - too -

4 *And made as He would eat me up -*

 As wholly as a Dew

 Upon a Dandelion's Sleeve -

 And then - I started - too -

5 *And He - He followed - close behind -*

 I felt His Silver Heel

 Upon my Ankle - Then my Shoes

 Would overflow with Pearl -

6 *Until We met the Solid Town -*

 No One He seemed to know -

 And bowing - with a Mighty look -

 At me - The Sea withdrew -

Emily Dickinson, 1891

Comparing

Q2 Using the poems on page 16, choose which paragraph below best compares the main idea in each.

   a) Both poems convey the main idea that the sea can have human qualities, and in this they are quite similar. But the way the poets go about it is very different.

   b) Both poems are about the sea being like people. In the first poem, Keats talks about the way the sea can make you feel better if you're stressed out. In the second poem, Dickinson takes her dog for a walk on the beach and thinks the sea is a man. Both poets should get out more.

   c) Both poems present an image of the sea as a companion, who is 'mighty' and all-encompassing. However, Keats also describes the sea as being gentle, and offering a soothing solace to those who may be world weary. In contrast, Dickinson personifies the sea much more overtly, and depicts it as a powerful male figure who offers her momentary, playful companionship.

Q3 Read the poems through again and answer the following questions:

   a) Which poem encourages people to seek solace in the sight and sounds of the sea?

   b) Which poem uses the sea as a metaphor for a man?

   c) Which poem includes images of fantastical beings?

   d) Which poem describes the sea's movement?

Q4 Write a few paragraphs comparing and contrasting the language used by each poet in the first parts of each poem (lines 1-4 Keats, and stanzas 1- 2 Dickinson). Don't forget to say how the language relates to the main idea outlined in Q2, and give examples.

Q5 Copy out these aspects of style and structure and match them with the explanations of their effect in the poems.

a) Irregular rhythm	i) Helps to move the 'story' along
b) Regular rhythm	ii) Evokes fluidity of the sea
c) Enjambment	iii) Don't allow time to reflect
d) Lots of short verses	iv) Convey a completed picture
e) Undivided sections	v) Increases the pace
f) Alliteration	vi) Slows down the pace

Q6 Using your answers from Q5, write a paragraph to compare the style and structure of each poem, and explain how this relates to the ideas of the sea in each.

Q7 Using the information you've got already from the questions above, and your own examples from the texts, write about a page to answer the following question:

> What methods do Keats and Dickinson use in order to describe and convey their ideas about the sea, and how do they compare with each other?

Compering is more fun — you get to make fentestic jokes...
Brrrr...is there a chilly draught in here, or is the evil spirit of Comparing Questions passing through?...

Making Your Argument Convincing

Q1   In each of the boxes there's a different version of a paragraph written in an argument essay. One uses evidence powerfully and one just doesn't get it right.

a)   Which of these paragraphs uses facts without getting bogged down in them?

i)	Out of the sample questioned 90% were in favour of the name change while only one person out of every fifty thought the new name difficult to remember.	ii)	The vast majority of people are in favour of the change of name and also think the new name will be easy to remember.

b)   Which one of these paragraphs uses an expert opinion backed up with a quotation?

i)	Doctors are keen for people to improve their health by taking more exercise. A representative of the British Medical Association said: "Being overweight and a couch potato leads to many health problems and shortens life."	ii)	Lots of people feel that men and women should take more exercise. This would help with fitness.

c)   Which of these two paragraphs uses real-life examples to support what it says?

i)	High exam grades can be very useful. Getting a good GCSE grade in English can improve a student's future prospects.	ii)	A 'C' or above in English gives 16 year olds a much wider choice of courses in the sixth form or at college and increases their chances of becoming high earners. It also supplies a sense of achievement and confidence that will help them make the most of every aspect of their lives.

Q2   The paragraph in the box below is not very effective — it sounds vague, uncertain and weak. Rewrite it to sound more definite.

> I feel it might be a good idea to pay an official reward to successful GCSE students. Maybe it would encourage some to greater efforts.

Q3   Now develop the argument by writing another paragraph to follow on from the one in Q2. Put forward logical reasons why paying GCSE candidates a reward will help them, their schools and society in general.

You don't just have to use factual proof well — you've got to keep your argument clear and logical too.

Making Your Argument Convincing

In order to make your argument writing effective don't forget the four top tips:

1)   Make a special point of being courteous and respectful to people with different opinions.

2)   Use "we" and "you" to make your reader feel personally involved in what you are saying.

3)   Rhetorical questions make people feel they already agree with you. Why not use them?

4)   Say things in threes. It's powerful, forceful and punchy.

Q1   In the box below there is a very poor piece of argument writing. Rewrite it taking account of the four top tips given above. You should be able to expand it into three or four paragraphs.

> Sixteen-year-olds should be given the vote and if you don't think so you're stupid. Lots of people agree with this idea and feel that sixteen- and seventeen-year-olds are often just as responsible and involved in their communities as older teenagers. After all, people can get married or join the army at 16.

Q2   Read these paragraphs. Write down what top tip each one uses to make it convincing.

a)   UHT milk is a foul-tasting product that should not be forced on anyone. I am, however, well aware that sincere and well-meaning people, no doubt including many of my readers, support its use on the grounds of convenience and cost.

b)   I beg them to reconsider their position. We all want cheap, safe and convenient food. However, does that justify making people drink this stuff?

c)   Is it right to expect people to drink something they dislike?

d)   UHT milk is unnatural, unpalatable and disgusting. You can help to see it banished from every kitchen in the land.

Retch or swallow? You decide.

Q3   Use the four top tips to write a short response to someone who has said that all teenagers are lazy.

You could begin:

> *Mr Jones may have had unfortunate experiences with teenagers but he cannot fairly conclude that all teenagers are the same.*

Think About Your Readers

Q1   The school fund-raising committee is drafting a letter for pupils to take home, asking for contributions to help fund a new school swimming pool. Use their notes to help you write three paragraphs for the letter.

1) Who are the readers?

- parents

- other close relatives of pupils

2) What will their worries and concerns be?

- pool needs to be built quickly if their child is to benefit from it

- people need to feel they are getting something for their money — maybe put names on tiles at the poolside for anyone contributing over £25

3) What will they say to argue against the idea?

- there is a public swimming pool only four miles away which the school has hired two mornings a week for years

- a swimming pool will be a dangerous hazard on a school site

Q2   Write an essay plan for this persuasive writing task.
Organise your planning notes under the same three headings used above.

Write an article for a local newspaper arguing that more money should be spent on libraries so they can improve internet access for all.

Q3   Write an essay plan for this persuasive writing task.
Organise your planning notes under the same three headings used above.

Write an advertising leaflet persuading people to take holidays in your local area.

Q4   Look carefully at the notes you have made. Now choose either the task from Q2 or the task from Q3 and write the piece in full using your notes to help with planning.

*Don't forget the topics covered on pages 18 &19
about making your argument <u>convincing</u>.*

Analysis Essays

Good analysis writing is:
1) *Clear and organised*
2) *Sounds neutral and detached — <u>never</u> say 'I' or 'we'.*
The aim is to make your writing sound trustworthy and unbiased.

Q1 Look at the pairs of sentences in the boxes below. One uses the first person ('I' or 'we') and the other is more detached and neutral. Write down the neutral sentence from each pair.

a)
There are often real problems of misunderstanding between parents and teenage children.
We all know that parents misunderstand their teenage children.

b)
I feel really upset when I read about animals being kept in horrid conditions in zoos.
Confining wild animals in zoos is considered cruel and disgraceful by many people today.

c)
Attitudes vary greatly but older people are usually more disapproving than younger people of swearing in public.
My grandfather is really shocked if I use offensive language in his hearing but I feel it is acceptable to use swear words.

Q2 Now look at the three sentences in the box below. Each one is in the first person and is much too personal and emotional for an analysis essay. Write a new sentence to replace each one. Your sentence must use the third person and sound detached, trustworthy and neutral.

a) Canned laughter on TV comedy shows sounds false and artificial and I hate it.

b) I feel very strongly that school canteens should serve breakfast so all kids can make a good start to their classroom work.

c) People make judgments about teenagers like me just because of the way we dress and I really can't stand it.

Q3 Write a paragraph on an issue that really makes your blood boil. Make it as angry and personal as you like. Then rewrite it in proper analysis style.

That ain't no backstreet sister — that's an alley sis...

So keep your cool when you're writing analysis essays. Otherwise you'll sound like you're just ranting and don't really have any idea what you're talking about. Which would be a shame.

Using Evidence

Q1   Write down which points you think are well-supported.

a)   Women drivers are worse than men because my Dad says so.

b)   Police report that two hundred people were wounded,
but hospitals admitted closer to five hundred that afternoon.

c)   It's disgraceful that children swear. When I was young, we wouldn't have dared.

d)   Yet another study, the fourth this year, has failed to find a
conclusive link between on-screen violence and viewers' habits.

Q2   Write out these first paragraphs in full by matching each opening statement to its evidence.

Opening Statements

a)   Boys are consistently out-performed by girls.

b)   Slouching can also lead to problems later in life.

c)   It was not just the final scoreline which indicated the better side.

d)   Athens cut traffic volume with remarkable results.

e)   Children are getting fatter.

Evidence

i)   *A quick glance at all the statistics, from amount of possession to the number of bookings —
shows that United were struggling that day.*

ii)   *Not only have exercise levels dropped in the last twenty-five years, but 87% of 13-16
year olds put TV viewing or playing computer games amongst their top three hobbies.*

iii)   *Almost overnight, levels of carbon monoxide halved.*

iv)   *56% of all back-pain sufferers in their fifties, admit to having had poor posture as teenagers.*

v)   *For the fifth year in a row, their performance in all exams, across a majority of subjects,
has been the weaker of the two genders.*

Q3   Using examples a) to e) in Q2, write out which of the following evidence **does not** wander off the point.

a)   Some think that more work needs to be done on researching different
learning styles of girls and boys.

b)   It might make you look like a bloke I saw once in the street, down
near the shopping centre. I remember it because it was the day I
dropped my wallet and had to go to the police station and report it.

c)   And their new strips look great — that colour really makes them
stand out amongst other teams in the league and it matches my car.

d)   Cars are allowed into the city centre on alternate days, depending on
whether the registration number ends in an odd number or an even number.

e)   And some of them are really noisy too. My neighbour has two kids and they shout all the time.
Some of us have complained about them, but it doesn't seem to make any difference.

Making It Clear

Q1   Look at this essay plan and copy out the points in a logical order.

> ### Explain how to find information on the internet
>
> - choosing key words for search
> - conclusion
> - scanning through search results for relevant sites
> - calling up a search engine
> - introduction

Q2   All these explanations have missed out stages. Copy them out and fill in the missing parts, choosing from the selection below.

    a)   While I am away, you need to feed the goldfish too. Add three pinches of it to the water every morning and two every evening.

    b)   Halve it. Take each half in turn and slice finely from the top through to the bottom. Further chop the slices if finer pieces are required.

    c)   Select the correct programme on the washing machine and load the correct amount of detergent. Once you have sorted your clothes into whites and colours, load just one pile. Then hang your clothes out to dry.

First, peel your onion.

Start the wash and let it run to the end of the programme.

You will find the fish food on the kitchen window sill.

Q3   Write out the examples below, underlining the complex or technical words and phrases.

    a)   It is a journalist's job to elicit information.

    b)   The students need to write back their files to the hard drive.

    c)   Sautée the potatoes in butter just before serving.

    d)   Once the undercoat is dry, apply the gloss paint.

    e)   "The full-back is nutmegged there — a real treat."

Q4   Using the examples in Q3, and a dictionary if you need to, re-write the sentences in clearer English.

Q5   For each of the readers below, describe some mobile phone functions of your choice, and how to use them.

    a)   Somebody your own age.

    b)   An adult who has a new model of phone.

    c)   An elderly person who has never used a mobile before.

Introductions and Conclusions

Q1   Write a sentence to say what makes each of these a good introduction.

a)   Ever wondered what it would be like if you stopped brushing your teeth? This article
     will explain the various stages that your teeth would go through if you did just that.

b)   What is the truth behind the studio gates? We delve into the secret world of Hollywood
     to uncover some amazing facts about film-making that we bet you never knew.

c)   You either love them or you hate them. We look at why McDuncan's is such a
     controversial fast food chain for some, while being a part of every day life for others.

Q2   Write a sentence to say what makes each of these a good conclusion.

a)   And so, if you are ever thinking about skimping on your dental hygiene, just remember the
     process to decay could begin with one tiny morsel of trapped food, and end up in a whole
     set of false teeth. That's something you'd have to live with for the rest of your life.

b)   Having seen the networking and personal influence that the studios and their
     stars use, we think it is astonishing that any films ever make it as far as the cinemas.

c)   Surely, on the evidence given, responsible people have to combine their strength of feeling
     and stop this multi-national from creating so much chaos in the third world — now.

Q3   These conclusions are all a bit feeble. Use the techniques from Q2 to rewrite them.

a)   It looks as though everyone has different opinions. Some think that we
     should join the Euro and others think it is a bad idea. Others think it
     doesn't matter. It is just impossible to say what people think.

b)   In conclusion, I have shown that there are many reasons for abolishing
     mobile phones in school, but also some reasons for keeping them.

c)   At the end of the war, Churchill was voted out of power, which might
     seem surprising to us today. People were not very grateful. Being a
     politician is not a very secure job even if you are good at it.

Q4   First decide whether each of these notes is for an introduction or a conclusion.
       Then write out the introduction or conclusion in full making it as good as you can.

a)   Spanish team always had potential, but, until recently, never lived up to it. We ask what changed.

b)   Banana crop is essential, but young people are choosing to leave rather
     than work in the banana groves — islanders must consider alternatives.

c)   Crochet not a new hobby, image is changing, more young people
     learning — article explores its appeal.

Oh, charmed, I'm sure...

Informing, explaining and describing is all about being clear. Making sure your readers understand.
Leaving no room for doubt. Being entirely unambiguous. Getting the facts straight. Laying all your cards out on the table...

Say What Happened

Q1   Write the correct letter under headings "Time", "Circular" and "Quest".

Look out — some of the stories could fall in more than one category.

> 1)   Time = following events over the weeks or years
> 2)   Circular = at the end things are similar to how they were at the beginning
> 3)   Quest = the main character travels in search of something

a)   The story follows the journey of a little dog left behind when its owners move. The dog travels through towns and villages, making friends and having adventures as it goes. It ends happily.

b)   The story begins in 1902 with the birth of a boy called Peter. The book follows his growing up and ends in 1918 with his experiences as a soldier in France in the First World War.

c)   Jedda is a warrior prince and when his sister is kidnapped by the evil Grolkons, he sets out to rescue her. The story tells of his adventures on the way.

d)   Danny and Petra wander into an old house and can't get out.
They stumble on a secret passageway leading to endless catacombs.
In each new chamber they discover a new adventure, but will they escape?

e)   Cathy is unhappy with her lonely life in a small northern town. She sets out to try and change it. The story follows all her failed attempts. Finally, her acting gets her a job out of town. When she gets to the new place she finds out it is similar to her home town and she hasn't moved on.

f)   The Stanleys are a happy family who live in a tumble-down house, and have a chance to leave when they inherit an old farm. The family is divided as some want to stay. The decision to go gradually destroys their happiness. Now, their house is in good condition, but they are in ruins.

Q2   Rewrite these three different starts, making something unexpected, sudden, or dramatic happen.

> a)   Julian opened his eyes and yawned.
>
> b)   It had been drizzling all day without stopping.
>
> c)   Lisa smiled through her veil at her husband-(very soon)-to-be.

Q3   Copy out the following openings based on some of the synopses in Q1 and underline any details you think are not relevant to the story.

a)   Fritz was to have many names over the next few months, not that he or Lucy, his owner, knew anything about it, of course. Lucy loved dancing and horses and her favourite colour was amber. She also loved Fritz, her dear little dog.

b)   Cathy was sick of it all — the constant rain, the grey streets and the grey people. She was in good health and had her ears pierced. She needed an escape route. Her mother had been a great fan of toffee. She needed something to aim for in life and the stage was where she was headed.

c)   Mr. Stanley sighed as another lump of plaster fell from the wall. They had painted the walls pink a few years ago. He shook his head and wondered when they could escape this old wreck which his wife just happened to love.

Go Into Detail

Q1   Copy out the sentences and the settings which match them, and write down how you could tell.

a)   *He narrowed his eyes and stared at the newcomer's spurs.*

b)   *"Give me my top hat, madam — I simply can't go to the theatre without it."*

c)   *The rain lashed against his oilskins and icy waves crashed down around him.*

d)   *She rubbed her calloused hands all over with the chalk, then turned to the judges and raised one arm straight. She was ready for the final stage.*

Settings
(i)   Victorian England

(ii)   the Wild West

(iii)   a gymnastics competition

(iv)   a North Sea trawler

Q2   Write down the **irrelevant** details from these descriptions.

a)   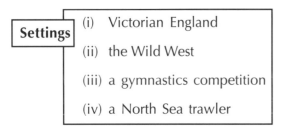 The roof tiles were piled dangerously high with snow, but Ned didn't know. Frank was washing his car down the road. Ned strode about in the garden, practising his big bass drum as usual, ignorant of the tottering mass above him.

b)   The chair was bright yellow and had four plump red cushions on it. Tracy sat down and narrowed her evil eyes.

c)   Michael had never seen Arabella look so stunning. It was quite warm and the evening sky was tinted with purple. She was wearing a red velvet dress and gold slippers.

Q3   Brighten up these segments of stories with descriptions which use the senses. Try to use each sense at least once, but don't overdo it.

a)   The fire destroyed the two-storey house within hours.

b)   It was the best pizza Digby had ever sunk his teeth into.

c)   Martin searched in the dark for the hammer and gasped in horror when something suddenly yelped.

Q4   Add interior monologues to create more believable characters in these extracts.

a)   Richard stepped up to the penalty spot, gulped nervously and hit the ball wide.

b)   Karen felt the hand on her shoulder and realised that she had wandered out of the shop with the dresses in her hand.

c)   Above his head, the blade of the guillotine glinted in the sharp autumn air.

Pace and Style

Q1   Read these extracts and think about the pace. Write down whether each one is fast or slow.

   a)   *Will gasped. He saw a glint of light. He heard the hiss of steel. He didn't stand a chance.*

   b)   Corrie knew she would eventually have to do something about the pile of work that towered in the far corner of the room. Just for now, though, she stretched out on the sofa and promised herself that she wouldn't get up until she had finished the next chapter.

   c)   *The hare darted through the thicket. The hunting dogs were after it, a pack of them, their slavering tongues lolling grotesquely, their bloodthirsty yelps alerting the hunters. Would they keep up, lose the scent, or fall behind?*

   d)   The rainbow slowly dazzled its colours in front of them, stretching across the sky in a beautiful, artistic brush stroke of glorious hues.

   e)   *He knew the best way to drown someone was to wait till they'd breathed out. That way their lungs would be empty of air, vacant, useless sacs, unable to support life for longer than 30 seconds...*

Q2   Write an explanation of why the following similes work or don't work.

The object and what it's being compared to have to have things in common.

   a)   The winter branches, like inverted, cancerous lungs, reached up into the white sky.

   b)   Val swept into the room like a fish swimming at night.

   c)   Yvonne stretched her arms towards the lifeboat like an impassioned conductor, desperate to reach the safety within it.

   d)   The new wood floor was as shiny and warm-looking as a kiwi fruit.

Q3   Rewrite the sentence for a) – d), replacing "walked" with more accurate verbs.

   Monty walked into the room.   a)   as if he was late   b)   as if he was happy

                                     c)   as if he was angry   d)   as if he shouldn't be there

Q4   Copy out the examples, underlining different characters' view points in different colours.

   a)   Judith hated it when he got like this and threw herself on the sofa. Richard ignored her completely. She would never understand how he felt. Never!

   b)   The black knight knew the last of his strength would leave him soon. The white knight saw the axe raised above him. He had to move or he would die from the blow. The black knight swung with all his might, yelling as he aimed for his sworn enemy. This was his last chance for revenge.

Let me tell you a story...

You got your original writing sorted. You became the new Michael Crichton — wrote your first blockbuster aged sixteen, retired, and never did a GCSE in your life... Ah, if only it wasn't just fiction.

Reading the Question

Q1   Write down a definition for each of the words below.
If you're not sure, use a dictionary to check on the meaning.

> compare   contrast   communicate
>
>   discuss   list
>
>   explain   select   convey

Q2   These are the four main types of question you get in the exam.

> a)   Checking you've understood the facts of the text.
>
> b)   Checking you understand the purpose of the text,
>   e.g. to explain something, or describe or sell a product.
>
> c)   Asking you to show you can see the difference
>   between fact and fiction in the text.
>
> d)   Asking you to explain how language has been used to
>   get the effects the writer wants.

Look in magazines, newspapers, backs of cereal packets, other food packaging, CD/DVD/video cases, instruction books for games, and reference books.

Find three different non-fiction texts. Pretend to
be the examiner who writes the exam questions.
Write four questions about the texts, one each for a) – d).

Writing questions is a bit weird but it will help you see where the examiners are coming from.

Q3   Write down which question from Q2 would be worth the
most marks, and which would be worth the least marks.

Q4   Invent a silly rhyme or a sentence that will help you remember these three points.

> 1) Read the question before the text.
> 2) Think about how many marks the question is worth.
> 3) Underline the key words in the question.

Reading the Text and Making Notes

Q1   a)   Find a feature article from a newspaper or magazine. It can be on any topic but most paragraphs should have more than two sentences and it should be at least seven paragraphs long.
Cut it out and stick it onto a plain piece of paper to give you space for note making.

[Remember a feature article is not a news story but an article giving background and details about some story or issue.]

     b)   Sum up the central idea of the article in one sentence.
Write it near the top of your page.

     c)   On the article itself and on the plain sheet of backing paper, underline key words and make notes to show how the writer has organised the ideas.
You might want to pick out key points, comment on language, comment on the tone, look for any use of humour and comment on variations in sentence length.

     d)   Look for an example of fact and an example of opinion. If either fact or opinion are missing from the article can you explain why? e.g. A gossip column might contain few facts and a news report of recent events might contain no opinions.

Q2   a)   Find another article of a similar length and style to the one you used for Q1.

     b)   Whom do you believe to be the writer's intended audience and what is the purpose of the article?

     c)   Use underlining and notes to help you understand how the article has been put together.

     d)   Comment on the ideas, tone and language used in the article.

     e)   Do you think the article is successful and interesting?

Writing Your Answer

The best way to start an answer is by rewording the question into a statement.
That way you can be sure you're answering the question.

Q1   Look at the question and decide which opening line is better. Write down why.

> *Question: How does the leaflet 'Saltburn Smugglers' try to*
> *make the museum sound interesting to readers?*

a) I think the Museum sounds very good and I would like to go there.

b) The 'Saltburn Smugglers' leaflet makes the museum sound interesting by using a mixture of fact and hints of sinister, mysterious legends which it backs up with intriguing pictures that are not always fully explained.

Q2   Look at the question and decide which opening line is better. Write down why.

> *Question: Explain how the letter from the charity tries to persuade people to donate money.*

a) *The Charity letter uses short paragraphs to make its ideas easy to read and therefore likely to persuade people to give money but also explains in detail how the money will be spent and gives a case study to show what a difference a small donation can make.*

b) *The Charity letter is trying to persuade people to give money to a good cause.*

Answers should be:
1) Precise — saying exactly what you mean and what the question asks for.
2) Complete — covering all the points needed.
3) Short — so long as you get all your points in.

Q3   Read this exam answer. The points it makes are OK but it's very waffly. Rewrite it so it's shorter and clearer.

> *Question: How does the leaflet 'Saltburn Smugglers' try to make the museum sound convenient to visit?*

The leaflet says there is parking at the museum. This is useful for people who are driving in cars and want to visit the museum. There is a playground at the museum and children who often go to museums do not really like museums but they like playgrounds so it is good for people who want to take children to the museum. The museum is near the railway station and the bus stops outside so that is useful for people who do not want to drive their cars and park in the car park. There is also a cafe so people will not have to worry about where to get their lunch. You can also phone and book a ticket in case there is a queue.

Writing Your Answer

Q1   Look at the sentences below. Some use evidence but the others try to make do with assertion, i.e. using an opinion as if it were a fact. Look for the tell tale words 'allegedly', 'apparently', 'possibly', 'supposedly' etc. and work out which are backed up by evidence and which are not.

a)   The popularity of gardening programmes on television possibly owes something to the boom in decorating and the improved weather of recent summers, which has made people feel they should make more of their gardens.

b)   The proportion of income spent on gardening products and plants has increased threefold over the last twenty years.

c)   Statistical evidence abounds to support the fact that sixteen year olds today are taller than sixteen year olds a hundred years ago.

d)   Teenagers today are allegedly much happier than teenagers of a century ago.

e)   It is popularly believed that up to three thousand large cats are at loose in more remote areas of Britain.

f)   Astronomers have calculated that the comet depicted in the Bayeux Tapestry is Halley's Comet which circles the Solar System every 75 years.

g)   By all accounts British holidaymakers are worse-behaved than those from any other European nation.

h)   Supposedly the secret ingredient in Inca chocolate was an extract from a little known hallucinogenic fungus.

Q2   Find two texts on the same subject. Write two paragraphs in answer to this question.

> *Compare the two texts and explain which one you think is more successful.*
> *Think about the differences between audiences and purpose as well as*
> *similarities and differences between the texts themselves.*

e.g. an encyclopaedia entry on a castle or cathedral and a tourist leaflet on the same place.

Writing About the Format of a Media Text

Q1   Find an example of a media text that you feel is aimed at young people and one which you think is aimed at an older and more professional audience. Make a list of the differences between them.

Q2   Look at these fonts. Write two or three sentences about each one giving the advantages and disadvantages of using the font to advertise "Finnegan's Funerals".

a)
Finnegan's Funerals

A font can be chosen because it looks:
- *honest and reliable*
- *cheerful and relaxed*
- *straightforward and honest*
- *modern and efficient*
- *etc. etc. etc. ...*

b)
Finnegan's Funerals

c)
FINNEGAN'S FUNERALS

d)
Finnegan's Funerals

e)
FINNEGAN'S FUNERALS

Q3   Write a paragraph about the layout and format of this book. Write about:

- the font
- use of colour
- layout
- use of pictures

Darling, wouldn't you love to work in the meed-yaa...

Most media texts are pretty devious. They want you to believe what they're saying, and they'll try anything to get you to believe it — from fonts to flattery. I think you're gorgeous by the way.

Standard English

Q1 Copy out the following sentences under the headings "Standard English" or "Non-Standard English".

   a) When I saw him, I was like, oh my God!

   b) Dinnae fash yersel' hen.

   c) This track was number one for six weeks in 1998.

   d) Whatever happens, I will keep my promise to you.

   e) Lenneisha and Zaria and me were chuffed to be asked to the party.

   f) I love the colour of that dress on you.

Q2 Copy out these sentences and underline the words and/or phrases that are <u>not</u> Standard English.

   a) If I had known that yesterday, I'd've never done it, you know?

   b) I was watching Big Brother, right, last night, right.

   c) I can't believe we lost – I was gutted!

   d) Fifteen minutes into the film, Nari chucked up everywhere.

   e) That'll be done in a jiffy, sweet as a nut.

   f) Jason – laters!

Q3 Rewrite these sentences using 'them' or 'those', and 'who' or 'which' in correct Standard English.

   a) You know them pens of yours? Let me see them.

   b) That is the man which sold most records in 1960.

   c) Do you still get them headaches?

   d) Them? They're horrible! Try them other shoes on instead.

   e) It was the poster of Will Smith who fell off the wall.

   f) It was *my* sister which won the high jump on Sports' Day.

Q4 Read the following examples carefully then rewrite them using Standard English expressions.

   a) Charlie went mad when he heard all them rumours about Tilly.

   b) Some random guy came up and asked me to snap him with my camera.

   c) Measure 4 Measure by Shakespeare does stuff about justice in it.

   d) It's not like watching the TV, it's, like, much better.

   e) I'm always telling you to be on time, innit?

Punctuation

Q1   Rewrite these sentences with capital letters and full stops in the right places.

   a)   the bicycle swerved to avoid the woman it was too late they collided

   b)   margaret has lived by the sea all her life it was a shock when she moved to the city

   c)   the park stretched away from the house its rolling fields were pleasant to the eye

   d)   i have change for the meter you can take these fifty pence pieces

   e)   my feet are aching let's stop and have a cup of tea

Hint: If you're not sure, say the sentence out loud. Listen carefully for the <u>pause</u> marking the end of a group of words.

   f)   don't worry if you see a lion they have already eaten today

Q2   Some of these sentences use commas correctly and some do not.
      Rewrite the ones that are wrong, correcting the mistakes.

   a)   Despite many appeals, including a high profile campaign over Christmas, drinking and driving figures have not substantially improved.

   b)   Turn left at the traffic lights then right then right again and it's just on the left.

   c)   I was late as, you might well imagine.

   d)   Books papers photos clothes and ornaments were thrown all over the floor.

   e)   Crithers McFosfate legendary horror writer died yesterday in his Californian home.

   f)   The horse hearing a loud noise took fright and bolted.

Q3   Each of these examples needs a colon or a semi-colon to make them into proper sentences.
      Copy them out with the correct punctuation.

   a)   You found an old friend__I found a new one.

   b)   He had a face you'd never forget__it was hideous.

   c)   It's raining__my hair will be ruined.

   d)   There's only one solution__you'll have to go there yourself.

   e)   This kit contains__twelve plastic pieces, a tube of adhesive, three colours of paint, two brushes of differing sizes and a set of instructions for assembly.

Q4   There is a dash or ellipsis in each of the sentences below. They should only be used for informal writing. Write out all the sentences which you think should be formal with better punctuation.

   a)   And then, when I looked back, Inspector, he was...dead.

   b)   You needn't think *I'm* doing your homework — you're on your own.

   c)   The second time Macbeth meets the witches he is brave — braver than before.

   d)   He denied it in front of witnesses — we can't make him confess, Sarge.

   e)   The image of Mrs. Park takes up most of the article … this technique is used to show her level of importance within the company.

Apostrophes

Q1   Change these phrases by writing them out again *without* the apostrophe.

         e.g.   *the cat's bowl = the bowl belonging to the cat*

    a)   Mum's briefcase   d)   the skeleton's bones

    b)   her pupil's progress   e)   Terry's satsuma

    c)   Arsenal's chances   f)   Hannah's calculator

Q2   Write two headings: 'Singular' and 'Plural'. Copy the underlined words under the appropriate columns.

    a)   the <u>children's</u> party   e)   the <u>soldiers'</u> guns

    b)   <u>Henry Kissinger's</u> wife   f)   my <u>mother's</u> <u>friends'</u> laughter

    c)   the <u>mice's</u> droppings   g)   <u>Colonel Hitchpankster's</u> men

    d)   the <u>flowers'</u> petals   h)   the <u>cows'</u> milk

Q3   Rewrite each sentence making corrections to its/it's where needed.

    a)   Goodness! Its three-thirty.

    b)   The car had a dent in its wing.

    c)   Its cold enough to be October.

    d)   Who knows what its called?

    e)   It's often confused for a parrot.

    f)   The factory belched smoke from it's chimney.

Q4   Rewrite the underlined words in full. Then, underline the letters the apostrophe replaced.

    a)   I <u>didn't</u> phone you last night because I was painting my goldfish.

    b)   You <u>shouldn't</u> let him cut your hair.

    c)   We <u>can't</u> leave now — <u>they'd</u> think we were rude.

    d)   <u>I'll</u> go in first. You wait here.

    e)   <u>You're</u> the last person <u>I'd</u> want to be stuck in a lift with!

    f)   You can tell them why <u>we're</u> so late.

Q5   Now make as big a list as you can of words where an apostrophe is used for omission.
       Use the words from Q4 to start you off.

Q6   Copy out the following sentences under two headings: 'Possession' and 'Omission'.

    a)   The donkey's straw hat blew away.

    b)   It wasn't me!

    c)   They are dad's boots.

    d)   He's fifteen, isn't he?

    e)   They'll win nothing this year.

    f)   The boys' room was tidy.

Speech Marks

Q1   Rewrite these examples using speech marks. And try out some more descriptive verbs instead of plain old 'said' while you're at it.

a)   DAVID: It's the third time I have come last in the 100m this year.

b)   CRAIG: I love mashed up bananas! They're great!

c)   JUDY: Do I look stupid to you?

d)   FRED: You have had your last chance, pal. It's payback time.

e)   KEELEY: Look after yourself. It's not *my* job, is it?

Q2   Rewrite these examples with capital letters in the correct places.

a)   Alex tore out of the room and shouted, "get down! It's about to blow!"

b)   "hold it right there, buster," yelled the cop.

c)   Kate shrieked, "that's the worst photo of me I've *ever* seen!"

d)   "hold the line, please," said Jade, "i need to write that down."

Q3   Rewrite these examples with either a comma, a question mark or a full stop in the blanks.

a)   "What do you think you're doing __" he shouted.

b)   She turned to him with tears in her eyes and said__ "You know I can't."

c)   She smiled and said, "This is the best pizza ever__"

d)   The fireman asked, "Are there any more people in there__"

e)   Mr. Brown turned to the hotel rep and cried__ "This is the worst holiday I have ever had__"

Q4   Write the following sentences out with every single little piece of punctuation correctly in place.

a)   you don't need to do that yourself said Emma

b)   scale the wall scale *that* castle wall scoffed the soldier you must be joking sir

c)   the judge cleared his throat and announced you have been found guilty of the murder of your wife

d)   the buried treasure is mine when we find it snapped the captain understand

e)   is it all right if he comes to school asked Mary pointing at her little lamb

f)   the wettest weather will be in the west smiled the weather girl

g)   select only the freshest ingredients for your larder simpered the TV chef

h)   if I pick the winner tonight I'll share my winnings with you said Dad

i)   fifteen hundred fans gathered in the centre of town to welcome the cup-winning team home announced the news presenter

j)   bob stuck his head out of the changing room and said can you bring me a size smaller please, dave

Negatives

Q1   Make two headings: 'Positive' and 'Negative' and copy out the sentences under the correct one. Look for clues in the words.

    a)   United will never win in Europe.

    b)   Barry forgot to bring his trainers for P.E.

    c)   Julian swore he wasn't at the scene of the crime.

    d)   Always wear a helmet on a scooter.

    e)   Never wear a live monkey on a scooter.

    f)   Use the juice of three apples.

Q2   Rewrite these negative sentences, changing them so that they use positive words.

    a)   Never look on the dull side of life.

    b)   I wouldn't start a long car journey without checking tyre pressure first.

    c)   You know Delaney never tells the truth.

    d)   Isn't that your house over there?

    e)   There were no parking spaces in the car parks in town on Saturday.

Q3   All of these sentences use double negatives. Rewrite them so they make better sense. There may be more than one option.

    a)   Nobody never went to my Alfred's grave.

    b)   None of my family isn't clever.

    c)   You shouldn't never stick your wet fingers in electric plug holes.

    d)   None of his kids look nothing like him.

    e)   Police! Don't nobody move.

    f)   I wouldn't never have done it if I'd known.

Q4   The answer to all these questions is 'none'. Write out the answers in full sentences.

    a)   How many holidays have you been on this year?

    b)   How many biscuits did you eat yesterday?

    c)   How many women perm their ears?

    d)   How many traffic jams were there in town on Sunday?

    e)   How many roads must a man walk down before he becomes grown up?

    f)   How many teeth do you have in your head?

Q5   Correct these sentences so they are clear.

    a)   I don't get no sleep at night.

    b)   My baby ain't got no money.

    c)   We never didn't love each other at all.

    d)   Nobody misses you like I don't.

    e)   I ain't sleeping none tonight.

    f)   Never give me no goodbye.

Writing Proper Sentences

Q1   All the verbs in these sentences are incorrect. Rewrite them without errors.

a)   I went back to my friend's house tomorrow, because he wasn't in today.

b)   My cousins comes to visit every summer.

c)   Every Wednesday next year, I went to Creative Sequinning classes.

d)   Here — I knows you, don't I?

e)   My brother play in a one man band.

f)   When I was young, I am the cleverest in my class.

Q2   Rewrite these examples, improving the sentences so they flow with style.

a)   Karen walked back the long way and so did Karen's mum.

b)   Hippos who can't hold their noses under water die by drowning and hippos who don't eat much die by getting too thin to live.

c)   The best way to catch a butterfly is to catch a butterfly when it is resting.

d)   Nobody knows who killed Sandra Bigginbottom but the person who killed her can't be very far away.

e)   It was midnight. Just after midnight there was a noise. Daveena heard it. Roxy just kept sleeping though.

f)   Too many cars are on the streets. There is a lot of traffic. There are lots of cars especially in the morning and the evening.

Q3   Now rewrite this paragraph, starting each sentence in a different way to make it more interesting.

> By the second day, Clarence noticed that the itch on his neck had grown swollen and red. By the third day, Clarence looked in the mirror and saw that the swelling had increased to the size of a golf ball. By the fourth day, the itching was unbearable and the lump was the same size as a bowling ball. By the fifth day, he had to hold his head to the left because the swelling was so huge he couldn't hold his head straight. By the last day of the week, Clarence realised that this itchy lump was no mere swelling. He realised it was no hideous allergic reaction to an insect bite. He realised that he was, in fact, growing a second head.

Q4   Rearrange the sentences in this paragraph so they're in clear chronological order.

> Brazil won. It was a brilliant final. Some people were sad that South Korea didn't make it to the final. I was sad that England got knocked out in the semi-final, though they just managed to beat Argentina in the quarter-final so there was a bit of consolation. I was pleased Ireland got beyond the second round too. I have to say, though, that the First Round is my favourite bit because there is football on telly three times a day and all the teams are full of hope and energy. I thought it was a terrible shame that Scotland and Wales did not qualify at all but I am sure they will next time.

Varying Sentences

Q1   Liven up these descriptions by using more varied and interesting adjectives.

     a)   I had a lovely birthday. I got loads of lovely cards and Mum gave me a lovely bracelet. Then, I had a lovely party and we ate a lovely cake.

     b)   This is absolutely the right time to move house. The market is absolutely full of people buying and selling and it's absolutely certain you'll get a good price. A good idea? Absolutely!

     c)   Look at these great trainers. I got them for a great price. They look great on my feet and they are great for comfort. If you got a pair, they'd look great on you too.

Q2   Make these paragraphs less boring by trying to vary the repeated words.

     a)   We went on a school trip last week. We went by coach to Dizzyland. When we got there, I went on six rides. The best I went on was called 'The Demon'. Dominic went on it four times. By the time we went home, we were calling him Demonic Dominic.

     b)   When I saw Rebecca I said that Amarpreet had said that she wasn't my friend. Rebecca said that she hadn't said anything like that and she didn't know why Amarpreet had said that to me. I got angry and said I didn't care what she said. Then she got upset and she said she didn't want to be my friend anyway.

     c)   I watched the TV last night. There was a football match on that I wanted to watch. Afterwards, I went out and watched my cat try to catch a bird. It didn't manage. It just watched it for ages.

Q3   Broaden your vocabulary — write out the 'fancy' word next to the simple word it matches.

a)	horrible	i)	nonsensical
b)	easy	ii)	uninteresting
c)	stupid	iii)	complex
d)	boring	iv)	unappealing
e)	difficult	v)	unchallenging

Q4   Use each of the fancy words from Q3 in a sentence which shows its meaning.

Q5   Rewrite the following examples changing some of the simple words for fancy ones.

     a)   The train left five minutes late.

     b)   Spain was quite a poor country until only a few years ago.

     c)   The magazine had loads of good stuff in it about make-up.

     d)   The midfield kept letting the other team through to attack.

     e)   You are much better at writing varied sentences now than you were at the start of this page!

I've got a broad vocabulary — it's extensive, expansive, er, wide...

Don't get bogged down using the same old words all the time. You want to make your work sound interesting and be fun to read. No really you do. It's everyone's burning desire. Surely.

Varying Sentences

Q1   Copy out these sentences and underline the two things being compared.

a)   Polly's hair was more golden than the sun.

b)   The bird's egg was smaller than a gobstopper.

c)   The oak tree's trunk was wider than a bus.

d)   Her voice was louder than a police car's siren.

e)   Rosie's eyes were brighter than twinkling stars.

Q2   Explain what the things in each part of Q1 have in common.

Q3   Try to compare the following with things to help the reader visualise them.

a)   a tower block

b)   a stream

c)   a football crowd

d)   a smile

e)   a hairstyle

For comparisons to really work, the two things need to have something in common.

Q4   Write two complete sentences for each pair of words, using 'as' in one and 'like' in the other.

e.g. feet, stilton → His feet smell as bad as a six-month old stilton.
→ His feet smell like six-month old stilton.

a)   cold   iceberg

b)   unfriendly   snarling dog

c)   exciting   roller coaster

d)   teeth   gravestones

e)   hair   mouldy straw

f)   quiet   mice

g)   voice   angel

h)   path   ribbon

Q5   Choose either type of comparison from Q4 to exaggerate these examples as much as you can.

a)   Martha is funny.

b)   The hill is steep.

c)   The boy usually eats a lot.

d)   The dog is smelly.

e)   The old man grumbles all the time.

f)   Briony is good at Maths.

g)   Yasmine is always tired.

h)   Anna never stops talking.

Varying Sentences

Q1 Spot the metaphor — make two headings: 'Literal' and 'Metaphorical' and copy these sentences under the correct one.

   a) By the last fence the jockey was carrying his horse.

   b) The mountain spring was clear and fresh.

   c) The baby cried all night.

   d) My party went with a bang.

   e) He always shoots my ideas down in flames.

   f) When I tell you things they go in one ear and out the other.

   g) She was so angry, her face went red.

   h) After her promotion, Kate was walking on air.

Q2 Write a list of as many metaphorical expressions as you can.

Hint: sports commentators and journalists are quite fond of using them...

Q3 Sometimes words can be used figuratively. Copy these sentences and underline the figurative word(s) in them.

   a) She sailed across the room.

   b) He was so angry! At half-time he exploded at them.

   c) Her face shone in delight.

   d) She rattled off the points in favour of the proposal.

   e) She sieved through the application forms quickly.

   f) The sergeant-major towered above the new recruit.

Q4 For the examples in Q3 explain what the figurative words are trying to suggest.

Q5 Replace the verb "walked" in the sentence below with a more figurative word to convey the emotions listed. Use the words from the box.

   He walked across the room.

   | sloshed | slimed | pirouetted |
   | crashed | limped | leapt | thundered |

   a) angrily

   b) sneakily

   c) apologetically

   d) confidently

   e) drunkenly

   f) impatiently

Q6 Add to the list and see how many different ways you can make him cross the room just by choosing good figurative words.

Language Words

Q1 Copy out these sentences and underline all the nouns.

a) The gardener took the shears and trimmed the hedge every Tuesday throughout the summer.

b) Sian and Cati had been friends for six years and there was a strong sense of loyalty and trust between them.

c) Clearly, the Directors must decide whether Paterson has enough skill to keep his place in the team.

d) All the things for the picnic were spread out on a tartan rug on the grass.

e) To build the cathedral, from the first brick to the last piece of wooden carving, took one hundred and thirty-three years.

f) Tragically, four field mice and a slow worm were killed when the river burst its banks.

Q2 Now use a different colour, or shape of line, and underline the verbs in the sentences in Q1.

Q3 Use the adjectives in the box to liven up the sentences below.

absorbing	colossal	bewildering	excruciating
minute	ostentatious	odious	attractive

a) There was a small rip in his trousers.

b) Look at that disgusting little dog.

c) I read this book in four days it was so interesting.

d) The maths test was too hard.

e) She dyed her hair bright pink just to be eye-catching.

f) They ran up a huge bill at the bar.

g) She bought a really nice jumper in that shop.

h) When I broke my finger the pain was really bad.

"My name's not Bill."

Q4 Make these sentences more visually descriptive by inserting an adverb of your own choice.

a) Rory walked into the room.

b) Felicity opened her mouth and shrieked.

c) Arabella curtseyed.

d) Bruce pointed at the crowd.

e) Quentin lay back in the hammock and sighed.

f) "How could you?" said Dilys.

g) "Why is it always me that has to wash the dishes?" asked Matt.

h) Chris was unaware that the bull was running at him and Owen.

Checking Practice

Q1   Rewrite this review from an Australian film magazine in Standard English.
You can change as many words as you want but must keep the same meaning.

> "Access Denied" is the fourth film by megastar Jean-Pierre Den Bosch to hit
> the screens in the new millennium. His fans won't be disappointed by this
> all-action, big-bucks extravaganza, but if you're looking for brain food, you'll
> need to find somewhere else to go for a nosh up.
>
> The story is simple. A computer programme magics up its own intelligence
> and turns against its programmers. Before long it is controlling every computer
> in the states and there's only one guy with the nous to stop it. So you don't
> need to be Einstein to work out the grand finale, but the effects and music are
> top notch. We gave it three Oz-stars out of five.

Q2   Poor punctuation has got this persuasive essay in a pickle. Re-write it correcting the mistakes.

> *in the last twelve years the state of the promenade has worsened to the point of
> near dereliction if you walk along on any day you will see overflowing rubbish
> bins litter fast food wrappers and spat out chewing gum on the pavements how
> long are we going to accept this before we begin to change it*
>
> *it is my proposal that we as proud residents of the town begin to make a
> difference to our own environment I say we all need to set an example if you see
> someone dropping litter don't just shake your head in disgust and walk on stop
> pick up the rubbish and put it in the nearest bin if you know the person why not
> tell them that you are unhappy with their behaviour*
>
> *it won't do any harm to take a more active approach to looking after our Town
> and it might just make things look a whole lot better*

*Even a fantastic piece of creative
writing won't get as much as a C
unless the punctuation is perfect.*

Q3   Re-write this extract adding some sophisticated punctuation where you see the underlines.

> The dry dust of the desert blew in through the open door_ it had drifted
> across the terracotta tiles_ long wisps of its sandy fingers reaching into the
> dark interior of Elianna's humble cottage.
>
> _ Mother. _
>
> A pitifully weak voice wandered through the body of the house_ a young
> voice, frightened and weary.
>
> But the voice would keep on calling_ it would get no response _ Elianna
> had left that morning and had no intention ever to return to the child or the
> house where she had lived all her life. Her child_s fate was now out of her
> hands_ Elianna_s decision was final.

Checking Practice

Q1   This local newspaper report needs some variety. Rewrite it, and liven it up.

LOCAL GIRL NANCY COULD GET PICKED FOR THE COUNTY

Nancy Tucker, from the village of West Utheringstood five miles outside Endville, came second at the East Crawlshire Draughts Trials on Sunday.

Nancy, 17, had everything to play for. Nancy said she was very nervous as she sat down to play her first game, but she was also nervous when she sat down to play the final game. She thinks she was more nervous for the final game than she was for the first game.

Nancy's Mum and Dad, Terry and Hilary, were both really pleased. "We are really pleased," said Terry. "Yes," said Hilary. Nancy was pipped to the post by last year's champion who comes from Busyton on the West side of the county. Nancy thinks she has proved that she is good enough to be picked for the County team.

The County team will be picked soon and announced next Thursday. The County team needs three players. Terry is confident that Nancy has done enough to get in. "I think she has done enough to get in this time," said Terry. "Yes," said Hilary. Nancy will go through to play for the county at the East of Britain trials in August if she gets picked. At seventeen, Nancy Tucker clearly has it all to play for.

Q2   Re-write the dialogue from this play so that it sounds more like real speech.
You can change as many words as you want, but not the meanings.

_Harold and Skipper are two old men who have known each other since they were in the army together during World War Two. They have allotments side by side in a plot on the outskirts of _____ (your town). This section of the play has them reminiscing about their return home from war._

HAROLD: _(sitting heavily on the upturned bucket)_ I did not expect things to turn out the way they did.

SKIPPER: You should not have expected anything. The people who were not fighting had no concept of what life was really like for soldiers like ourselves.

HAROLD: _(pushing back his cap and scratching at his scalp)_ But I _did_ expect, Skipper. I expected flags waving and crowds cheering, exactly like there was when we left, do you remember?

SKIPPER: _(clenching his teeth)_ Of course I remember. The train station was full of people who were staying safely at home. No wonder they were cheering.

HAROLD: You must not say that, Skip. Try not to be bitter.

SKIPPER: Why not? Why should I not?

HAROLD: It was a long time ago. It was almost fifty years ago, Skip.

SKIPPER: _(muttering)_ Well it still feels like it was yesterday to me.

You gotter be cruel to be kind (sucking teeth)...

So ALL you have to do is sweat blood over writing your essay, and then sweat blood checking it.
I think I'll send the examiners some flowers to say thanks for being such great guys and gals.

Answers

Answers for Pages 1 to 2

SECTION 1 — WRITING ESSAYS
Page 1 — Planning & Introductions

Q1 **Introduction**
- Way we live not just unhealthy for us — not good for the environment either.
- Need to change the way we live. (*It would be OK to save this point for the Conclusion too.*)

Middle
- Too much 'leisure' time spent sitting behind computers or watching TV and videos — too little exercise = increased risk of heart disease, and constant use of electricity causing pollution. Spend less time watching TV/using computers — do a bit more exercise for fun.
- Driving cars — not enough exercise, using up the world's oil and creating pollution. Can use public transport, or even better cycle or walk to work or shops.
- Busy work schedules mean less time to prepare proper food. Convenience foods don't have enough nutrients in them for a healthy balanced diet. Also convenience foods have more packaging — creates more rubbish. We can take time to prepare fresh food — healthier diet and less rubbish.

Conclusion
- Is possible to change the way we live by choosing more carefully what we eat, and by being more active. This will make our lifestyles much healthier, and be far better for the environment.

Q2 Modern lifestyles are becoming more unhealthy, and this is something which my Mum has been saying for ages. When I was in the shower last week, she said that I had been wasting loads of hot water. There is an increased risk of heart disease due to lack of exercise, and general ill health caused by poor eating habits. We can choose to walk or cycle to the shops or to work, instead of using up the world's natural resources. Increasingly, the way we live our daily lives needs to change, if we are to stop the damage we are doing to ourselves and the world around us.

Q3 *This question's open-ended, but here's a sample answer. Don't copy — write your own.*

a) The way we live is not only bad for our health; it is also having a dangerous effect on the environment. The way we live our daily lives needs to change if we are to stop the damage we are doing to ourselves and the world around us.

b) Many people do not question their use of cars. They use their cars even for very short journeys to work or to the shops, missing out on another valuable opportunity for exercise. Cars are one of the main sources of pollution in the UK. Cars also use up millions of barrels of precious oil every day. Although it is unavoidable to use cars from time to time, drivers could leave their cars at home for short trips, and cycle or walk instead.

c) By cycling and walking more and using our cars less, by doing more exercise for fun, and eating less convenience food we can make a difference to our own health and the health of the planet.

Page 2 — Formal and Informal Language

Q1 *This question's open-ended, but here's a sample answer. Don't copy — write your own.*

a) Shakespeare creates tension between Oberon and Titania in order to highlight the division between power and passion in the play.

b) In creating the character of Willy Loman, Arthur Miller highlights the ordinary working man's position in society. His inner turmoil evokes sympathy in the reader.

c) The images of snow and whiteness indicate the fact that it is winter, but also convey ideas about the poet's state of mind, such as isolation, suffocation and boredom. This stanza sets the mood for the rest of the poem.

d) Shakespeare questions the emphasis we place upon physical beauty by highlighting Demetrius's initial rejection of Helena.

Q2 *This question's open-ended, but here's a sample answer. Don't copy — write your own.*
Scientists have finally discovered a drug which can make you look younger! Recent research has shown that a substance found under the sea bed can make your skin 98% firmer. Proposals for the new pill, which would be made from a chemical found in coral, has sparked a row between the drug company big wigs, who stand to make a lot of money if the drug gets the go-ahead, and eco-warrior groups who say that the coral should be left alone.

Q3 *This question's open-ended, but here's a sample answer. Don't copy — write your own.*

a) The bright midday sun burst down upon the glassy sea, casting joyous reflections on the boats and people hovering about excitedly.

b) The spooky old house with twisted turrets and spindly windows loomed upon the lonely hill, enclosed by clawing vines and the shadows of watchful trees.

c) The majestic chestnut stallion strode across the finish line with triumph, then gracefully wandered around exhaling huge lungfuls of steam in the winter air.

d) Quickly forgetting their rumbling tummies, the children's' faces lit up with expectation as their eyes feasted upon the wonderful sight before them. The dining table was crammed full with colourful trifles, tasty sandwiches, bowls of crisps, wobbling jellies and fizzing drinks.

Answers for Pages 3 to 5

Page 3 — Giving Evidence & Quoting

Q1 a) After running about in the garden all day, Felix finally came indoors to eat his food. When Katy bent down to pat him, she noticed <u>pieces of red cloth sticking out from between his teeth which matched the colour of Pete's slippers</u>. Felix ate all of his food happily.

b) Patricia looked fantastic as she pulled up in her shiny new sports car. It was a beautiful day, and her neighbour Daniel was outside doing some gardening when she emerged from the car, shouting over to him 'Hey, Dan, what do you think of my new car?' At that moment, <u>Daniel turned on his lawn mower and pretended not to have heard her</u>.

c) The wind was blowing hard and Skipper Johnson had a <u>bad feeling in his stomach</u>. The <u>colour of the sky didn't look good</u> to him. He knew he had to tell the others that it might come to the point of <u>abandoning ship</u> within an hour, as he watched the waves crashing over the deck.

Q2 a) Mrs.Wittaker said, "If I don't get the children vaccinated, I could be putting their lives in danger." There are plenty of parents like Mrs.Wittaker who feel the same way. (Mrs.M.Wittaker, The News Today, 2002)

b) "There can be no excuses for children who do not get their homework in on time. I am prepared to stay behind after school to supervise detentions." Mr. Snodgrass, the chemistry teacher, had to make this clear after receiving only four homework books last Tuesday. (Mr.P.W.Snodgrass, Schools in Focus Weekly, 2002)

Q3 *This question's open-ended, but here's a sample answer. Don't copy — write your own.*

a) Mrs.Wittaker believes that if she doesn't get her children vaccinated then she could be putting their lives in danger. (Mrs.M.Wittaker, The News Today, 2002)

b) Mr.Snodgrass made it clear that there can be no excuses for children who do not get their homework in on time, and added that he was prepared to stay behind after school to supervise detentions. (Mr.P.W.Snodgrass, Schools in Focus Weekly, 2002)

Q4 a) There have been frequent criticisms of the country's leading football team recently, despite the fact that they are still at the top of the premier division. This comes after a remark made by a major sports journalist who described them on prime time television as being "dirty players with no real tactics." However, other pundits have put the recent wave of criticism down to jealousy of the team's success, and point out that it has certainly not altered their performance at all. "We are getting better after each game." The team's manager said yesterday.

b) A new flower has been named after the glamorous film actress, Suzie Starlet. The flower, now to be known as a 'Pink Suzie' was unveiled yesterday by its famous namesake at the annual flower show in Brighton. A flower show spokesperson described the now famous flower as "a beautiful pink and orange rose with a delicate perfume. "When asked how she felt about having such a flower named after her, Suzie Starlet gushed simply, "I'm flattered and honoured."

Page 4 — Writing in Paragraphs

Q1 a) new person and new place   b) new person speaking   c) new topic   d) new person

Q2 *It doesn't matter if your answers are slightly different — as long as there's a good reason for each new paragraph.*

a) Two years ago this building was derelict, awaiting demolition. Luckily two businessmen saw it and noticed its potential. They decided to buy it, despite many people thinking they were mad to take such a risk.
Now it houses a thriving restaurant, popular with A-list celebrities and it is impossible to get a table unless you know the maître d'.

b) Sarah was sitting in the common room, singing to herself and reading a trashy magazine. She was waiting for Gareth to pick her up and he was always late so she'd come prepared.
The door creaked and Paul came into the room, looking embarrassed. He had something to tell her and she wasn't going to like it.

c) "I'm afraid I'm sacking you, Pete," said Mr. Rogers sternly.
"But it was an accident Mr. Rogers — I swear. If I'd known I was going to set fire to the building I'd never have started smoking in the first place," cried Pete. He gave Mr. Rogers his most pleading, innocent look, but it was too late.
"I'm sorry, son, but this time you went too far."

Q3 *Check you started the second paragraph when you started writing about a new person, a new place, or a new topic.*

Page 5 — Writing in Paragraphs

Q1 *This question's open-ended, but here's a sample answer. Don't copy — write your own.*

a) *Second paragraph*: But then, there's no accounting for taste...

b) *Second paragraph*: The desire for more is even driving people to work longer hours and take less holiday...

c) *Second paragraph*: Some of the dangers of a mountain expedition can be avoided — if you prepare carefully.

Q2 a) The Bank of England has made an embarrassing discovery. It has had to halt distribution of the new £5 note after it was discovered parts of the note's design were disappearing.
The Bank stated that about 10 million of the new £5 notes had been distributed. The new note is the same size and colour as the old fiver.
"We understand a substantial proportion of the new notes are still in bank or Post Office branches and have not been issued to the general public," said a Bank of England spokesman.

Answers for Pages 5 to 7

b)   The most significant factor contributing to global warming is increased emissions of carbon dioxide, the main greenhouse gas. Extensive deforestation and fossil-fuel burning are leading to high levels of carbon dioxide in the air.

Increased emissions of methane are also contributing to the greenhouse effect, although on a far smaller scale than carbon dioxide. One reason for the increased emissions is the modern practice of intensive animal farming.

Q3   *This question's open-ended, but here's a sample answer.* **Don't copy — write your own.**

a)   A tasty burger or a takeaway pizza is always tempting, and when you eat that kind of food as an occasional treat there's nothing wrong with it. But if you make a habit of eating junk food the huge number of calories, high fat content and low nutritional benefits can have a serious effect on your health.

The perfect partner to a takeaway is a lazy evening in, watching a video. Again this could have serious effects on your health if you crash out on the sofa every evening. Our bodies need exercise to keep heart, lungs and muscles in good shape.

If we are to believe what we read in the papers, the number of unhealthily overweight people in Britain is on the rise.

It is up to each of us to change our lifestyles so that we eat less junk food and take more exercise if we want to stay healthy.

b)   Selina didn't like the sound of Grime High, and she didn't like the look of it either. She stood on the pavement looking up the steep steps at the gothic arch over the studded wooden door, and the bats circling round the towers with icy fear in her stomach.

Inside the secretary pointed Selina towards classroom 11B. It was at the end of a long dirty corridor. When Selina put her head round the door the teacher pointed with a long, gnarled finger to a desk at the front of the room. He didn't say a word. Neither did the other pupils. By the end of the morning Selina was beginning to feel very uncomfortable about being ignored. She was starting to wonder whether she'd done something incredibly offensive without even realising.

At lunchtime Selina decided to try and be friendly. She sat with a group of girls from her class in the lunch hall, but it wasn't till they were stacking their plates that one of them actually spoke to her.

"Hello, are you Selina? My name's Jo."

Suddenly everyone turned to Selina, asking her questions and making big efforts to make her feel at home. As they were walking back to the classroom Selina turned to Jo and said, "So why did everyone give me the cold shoulder this morning?"

"Hmmm, well...it's something the teacher likes to do. He's very shy, so he prefers new people to be invisible for a couple of hours so he can get used to the idea of them...we just didn't realise you'd arrived."

So on the plus side nobody hated Selina, but what stunts was the teacher going to pull this afternoon?

Page 6 — Writing Conclusions

Q1   d), c), b), a)

There can be no dispute that at the end of the play, we are left with the feeling that nothing significant has really changed. Estragon and Vladimir have episodes of activity throughout the play, and there are moments when it seems as though something will happen, or that the scene will change dramatically. The mere promise of change gives the play momentum, but the plight of the main characters does not change, nor does our perception of it. The writer creates a perpetual cycle of anticipation and boredom throughout the play which comes to represent the human condition.

Q2   <u>I couldn't really make my mind up at first, but I think that</u> at the end of the play, we are left with the feeling that nothing significant has really changed. <u>I found the play very boring.</u> Estragon and Vladimir have episodes of activity throughout the play, and there are moments when it seems as though something will happen, or that the scene will change dramatically. <u>In Act Two it looks as if something exciting might happen, but then the characters just go back to talking about Godot.</u> The mere promise of change gives the play momentum, but the plight of the main characters does not change, nor does our perception of it. The writer creates a perpetual cycle of anticipation and boredom throughout the play which comes to represent the human condition.

Q3   *This question's open-ended, but here's a sample answer.* **Don't copy — write your own.**

The difference between people who dance and those who don't is largely due to a question of confidence. Those with confidence find it easier to let go when dancing, and those less confident tend to avoid dancing. However, confidence can be developed over time if the person really wants to achieve a specific aim. Therefore, the main difference between people who dance and those who don't is probably down to a matter of choice as much as anything.

SECTION 2 — WRITING ABOUT LITERATURE
Page 7 — Answering Literature Questions

Q1   *   The way George Orwell was brought up.

*   Different types of farming methods.

*   One of the main characters.

Q2   a) Characters   b) Cultures and traditions   c) Writer's message   d) Writer's message

Q3   *This question's open-ended, but here's a sample answer.* **Don't copy — write your own.**

• Pig 3 acted more intelligently than Pigs 1 and 2.

• Pig 1 built house from straw. Pig 2 built house from twigs. Wolf blew down houses and ate pigs.

• Pig 3 knew bricks are heavier than straw and twigs — built his house from bricks. Wolf couldn't blow it down.

• Wolf intelligent too — climbed down chimney of Pig 3's house.

• Pig 3 ~~more intelligent than Pig 1, Pig 2 and Wolf~~. Puts pot of boiling water in fireplace, catches Wolf and kills him.

• Eventual defeat of Wolf due to intelligent behaviour of Pig 3.

Answers for Pages 8 to 9

Page 8 — Writing About Characters

Q1 a) ii)   A young, excitable school girl with lots of energy, who likes to have fun with friends.

b) iii)   A peaceful, elderly, but child-like man, who's happy to let his wife mother him.

Q2 *This question's open-ended, but here's a sample answer. Don't copy — write your own.*

> PUCK: Captain of our fairy band,
> Helena is here at hand,
> And the youth, mistook by me,
> Pleading for a lover's fee,
> Shall we their fond pageant see?
> <u>Lord, what fools these mortals be!</u>
> OBERON: Stand aside: the noise they make
> Will cause Demitrius to awake.
> PUCK: Then will two at once woo one;
> <u>That must needs be sport alone;</u>
> And <u>those things do best please me</u>
> That befall <u>prepost'rously</u>.

Puck is a mischievous character who likes to poke fun at mortals, and enjoys creating mishaps which make them appear absurd and stupid. He enjoys a position of power over the others.

Q3 *This question's open-ended, but here's a sample answer. Don't copy — write your own.*

a) *MONEY*: "I really can't get over how much money Mr.Wilkes is worth. I simply adore his beautiful house and flashy sports car. One day I'll be rich, too."

b) *JEALOUSY*: "Mrs.Wilkes and I were childhood sweethearts. If it weren't for her old man, we would be together again as if no time had passed between us. He thinks he's got it all, but it won't last."

c) *ANGER*: "I knew I didn't like the look of Mr.Wilkes the day he moved in next door and trampled all over my prize chrysanthemums. I had to pull out of the flower show after that, and I never got so much as an apology."

Page 9 — Writing About Characters

Q1 *This question's open-ended, but here's a sample answer. Don't copy — write your own.*

a) The Wicked Queen of Avalonia is actually a timid character, who suffered in silence for many years.

b) Mr.Finchley was actually a very generous character, who simply liked his privacy, and wasn't too keen on the local pub.

c) Mrs.Tabble is a character who appears to be motherly and kind, when she is actually bad tempered, and mean to her pet.

Q2 *This question's open-ended, but here's a sample answer. Don't copy — write your own.*

a) We can tell that the Wicked Queen of Avalonia isn't really wicked because when she is given the opportunity to seek revenge upon her cruel chiropodist, we are told that she '..thought it best to keep quiet about it all, not wanting to upset everyone.' We are told that she is innocent of the crime she faces execution for, and that she had suffered 'many years of ill treatment' at the hands of her chiropodist. She appears to be the victim in this story.

b) The fact that Mr.Finchley leaves all of his money to John the milkman makes us distrust the neighbours' opinion of him as 'greedy' and 'snobby.' The fact that Mr.Finchley '..just hadn't been the same' initially suggests that he had changed for the worse. However, the fact that he'd stopped going to the pub, and had put up a large fence around his house doesn't necessarily make him 'greedy' or 'snobby.' He obviously got on well with the milkman, and his final act of generosity proves this.

c) Katie's reaction of being 'surprised' and 'saddened' at seeing Mrs.Tabble kick her dog in the park makes us see the double-sided nature of Mrs.Tabble's character. Katie obviously was not expecting to see Mrs.Tabble behave in such an angry and cruel way, as she had been used to seeing the 'lovely' Mrs.Tabble, the '..kind old dinner lady' who had brought the children 'special sweets' on Fridays. From Katie's reaction, we can see Mrs.Tabble as being insincere, and not as 'kind' as she would like everyone at school to believe.

Q3 *This question's open-ended, but here's a sample answer. Don't copy — write your own.*

a) It was such a shock being arrested for stealing a loaf of bread, but I knew immediately that someone had set me up. I think the Cruel Chiropodist is in cahoots with the Baker of Avalonia. They just want me out of the way, so that they can build an empire together, with my money! I wouldn't say anything though, the despair it would bring to my family is just too much to risk. They'll get their come-uppance eventually!

b) It was great winning all of that money, as it allowed me to spend less time at work (and therefore less time at the pub on the way home) and more time indoors, looking after my sick mother. I had to build the big fence to protect all of the valuable jewellery I had bought for her. When she died, I became great friends with the milkman, as we were both working on the same charity project. It made sense to put him in my will.

c) Every Friday I bring special sweets for the children at school because I love to watch their little faces light up with excitement. When I saw Katie in the park during the summer holidays, I had just fended off a stranger's dog who had been trying to bite me viciously.

Answers for Pages 9 to 11

Q4   *This question's open-ended, but here's a sample answer. Don't copy — write your own.*
All these sources are equally reliable or unreliable. We would need to know more of the story before we could fully make up our minds about the Queen of Avalonia.

Page 10 — The Writer's Message

Q1   b)   What do you think Shakespeare is saying about love in Romeo and Juliet?

d)   What does Educating Rita tell us about the way society operates?

Q2   **Story**
• Marlow goes on a journey up the Congo River, where he eventually meets Mr.Kurtz, and experiences first hand the corruption of the wilderness and its people
• Ideas of corruption are explored on many levels throughout Marlow's narrative.

Characters
• Main characters are Marlow, who is travelling on behalf of a Belgian trading company, and Mr.Kurtz, an ivory trader who holds a position of power over the inhabitants of the area and is described in negative terms.
• Conrad uses the other characters mainly to symbolise different aspects of African and Western culture.

Tone
• One of sadness, anger, and a lack of optimism for the future.
• Conrad is scathing about Marlow's life in England.

Title
• 'Heart of Darkness' is a very negative title, and it suggests Conrad's ultimately pessimistic view of human existence and human nature.

Q3   b)   The heart of human existence is always susceptible to 'darkness' and corruption, and colonialism is an example of this.

Q4   *This question's open-ended, but here's a sample answer. Don't copy — write your own.*

a)   **Story**
• Goldilocks goes into the Three Bears' house and, tries their porridge, sits on each of their chairs, sleeps in each of their beds, and then runs off.

Characters
• Goldilocks — a spoilt, rude little girl who imposes upon the Three Bears.
• Three Bears — Mummy Bear, Daddy Bear and Baby Bear. A comfortable family, each with their own pieces of furniture.

Tone
• One of indignation — how can this girl be so rude as to wander into the Bears' house, test and reject what they have to offer, and behave in the way she does?

Title
• "Goldilocks and the Three Bears" suggests that Goldilocks is an individual, contrasted with a settled unit — the bears. Goldilocks' selfish individual behaviour contrasts with the Bears' cooperative behaviour. The name Goldilocks suggests the girl has blonde curly hair — it's easy to picture her as a spoilt little brat.

b)   Selfish behaviour is disruptive and upsetting. It's better to cooperate and think about others.

Page 11 — Different Cultures and Traditions

Q1   *This is where all the words come from and what they mean:*
bigibigi (=important , from Sranan — a Creole spoken in Surinam); dis marnin' = this morning (Caribbean accent); chifforobe = cabinet (Afro-American dialect); cumdach = shrine (Gaelic); laidak = rogue (Polish); everyting = everything (Caribbean accent)

Q2   *This question's open-ended, but here's a sample answer. Don't copy — write your own.*
People he teaches don't speak English as first language.
"Want to live elsewhere" suggests there are quite serious problems in this country.
Viktor — probably not an English name as spelt with a K not a C.
Goes for a drink in a cafe — not a pub.
Don't drive on the left in this country.
"muzhiks" — foreign word, could be from the language spoken in this country.
Laws aren't as strict as in this country — he's only joking but says people don't know what side of the road to drive on.
Has to bribe the harbour master and pay mafia — so there's quite a high level of corruption.
Weather sounds more extreme than here.
Must be quite a poor country as doesn't sound like the roads are surfaced.

Q3   *This question's open-ended, but here's a sample answer. Don't copy — write your own.*
The narrator describes his week job as "teaching English to people who want to live elsewhere". It makes it sound as though he finds his job pointless. He bluntly describes driving round the country roads as "hell". Clearly he would rather not do it.
He is not completely depressed about his way of life though. He jokes about the "stupid muzhiks" and makes socialising part of his business dealings with the Japanese sailors.

Answers for Pages 12 to 13

Page 12 — The Writer's Techniques

Q1 *This question's open-ended, but here's a sample answer. Don't copy — write your own.*

a) Julia huddled in close to the huge roaring fire to keep warm. Martin, the boy from the village, had said that he would be there at eight o'clock to take her out. It was now eight thirty, and Julia forced herself to turn and face the window, which looked out upon the lonely causeway, to see if she could spot his car headlights, but there was nothing. Branches scraped upon the window pane, and deep down Julia knew that the howling wind and torrential rain had kept Martin from coming to her rescue.

b) Julia waited by the magnificent, roaring fire in warm anticipation. Martin, the handsome boy from the village, had promised to be there at eight o'clock to whisk her off to a romantic rendezvous on the other side of the island. To her disappointment it was quickly approaching eight thirty. She rushed over to the window to see if she could catch a glimpse of her lover's shiny speed machine. The huge boughs of sycamore and early evening downpour obstructed her view, but she knew in her heart that Martin would get there, one way or another.

c) FEARS FOR MAN'S SAFETY AS TORRENTIAL RAIN HITS SEASIDE VILLAGE Julia Smith expected to see her friend at eight o'clock last night, but half an hour later he had not arrived. Unable to spot his car along the causeway, she immediately alerted emergency services.

Q2 a) i) A very organised woman who knows what she wants.

b) i) Short, simple sentences.   iv) Formal wording.   v) No fancy comparisons.

Q3 *This question's open-ended, but here's a sample answer. Don't copy — write your own.*

a) Julia sat in the <u>lonely old vicarage</u>, huddling in close to the fire, <u>trying to keep warm</u>. The <u>huge stone walls</u> were <u>damp</u> and gave off a <u>mouldy stench</u>. Trying not to move, she forced herself to turn and face the <u>cobweb covered</u> windows, which looked out onto the darkness of the <u>windswept causeway</u>.

b) We are supposed to feel that Julia is uncomfortable being on her own in the 'lonely old' vicarage, which is cut off from the rest of the land by a 'windswept' causeway. Her discomfort is brought out further in the fact that she finds it hard to keep warm, as the walls are damp and give off a 'mouldy stench.'

Q4 *This question's open-ended, but here's a sample answer. Don't copy — write your own.*
When Martin was six or seven his mother spent an hour looking for him in the park where he was supposed to be playing with the other children, before giving up and going home to call Pete's mother. Martin had forgotten to tell his mother that he was going over to Pete's to play computer games after school. He just didn't think about how worried his mum would be. She only hoped he would never disappear like that again.

Page 13 — Useful Literature Words

Q1 **Simile**
- The woman in the pub was howling like a banshee.
- Mark's father was as nice as pie when he came home.
- The plane soared effortlessly as a bird into the blue sky.
- The sea was like a pane of glass.

Metaphor
- My boss is an immature little baby.
- The people of the world are tenants and God is the landlord.
- Jason's new bike was the Rolls Royce of mountain bikes.
- The Moon is the mother of the planets.

Q2 iii) Sarah's desire to be able to walk again.

Q3 *This question's open-ended, but here's a sample answer. Don't copy — write your own.*
Mr. Jones loved his children. He worked hard in the office all day to make sure he had enough money to keep them well fed. One day, he decided to build a big house for his family to live in, so he would know that they would all be safe. A jealous neighbour, Mr. Hamilton, lived on his own in a small house, and didn't like the fact that Mr. Jones had so many children and a nice big house. One night, when he knew they would all be out, Mr. Hamilton set fire to his neighbour's lovely house. Mr. Jones was devastated. The fact that they no longer had a home meant that all of his children had to be separated out among different friends and relatives whilst he started saving for a new house from scratch.

Q4 *This question's open-ended, but here's a sample answer. Don't copy — write your own.*
It is ambiguous whether John likes the food because the fact that he "couldn't eat another thing" could mean either that he's eaten too much and can't fit anything else in, or that he couldn't eat another thing because it tasted vile to him and it would make him sick. The fact that he was "very interested" in knowing the ingredients that Madge had used, could mean either that he wanted to try and make the recipe at home because it was so delicious, or that he wanted to know where she might have gone wrong whilst cooking, and was wondering if she had put something disgusting or harmful in the food.

Q5 Christopher had always been a brainy grade-A student. So everybody had <u>really expected him to fail disastrously</u> at the children's spelling competition.

Sally was <u>her usual inconspicuous self</u>, with a bright pink and purple t-shirt and yellow striped jeans.

Answers for Pages 14 to 17

Page 14 — Reading Plays

Q1 *Tragedy*: King Lear   *Comedy*: Twelfth Night   *History*: King Henry V

Q2 a) ii), b) iv), c) i), d) iii)

Q3 **This question's open-ended, but here's a sample answer.** *Don't copy — write your own.*

Design: A small, darkly lit room, with boxes of used tissues scattered around the floor. An unmade bed with clothes strewn on top of it.

Action: Benedick creeps quietly into Beatrice's bedroom, taking care not to startle her. Beatrice lies weeping on the edge of her bed.

Benedick: (With arms outstretched to her) Lady Beatrice, have you wept all this while?
Beatrice: (Pushing him away) Yea, and I will weep a while longer.
Benedick: (Quietly stepping back) I will not desire that.
Beatrice: (Holding her hand in the air defiantly) You have no reason; I do it freely.

Page 15 — Words to Use When You're Writing About Poetry

Q1 a) <u>Cute Carly</u> loved the <u>cuddly clown</u> she got for <u>Christmas</u>. *Alliteration*

  b) <u>Sheila leaped</u> across the <u>heath</u> to where the <u>sheep</u> were fast <u>asleep</u>. *Assonance*

  c) The snake <u>hissed</u> at the guide as he tried to <u>hush</u> the noisy children behind him. *Onomatopoeia*

  d) <u>Rachel ran</u> across the <u>reading</u> room with a <u>thud</u>, as the <u>buzzing bees</u> chased her. *Alliteration and onomatopoeia*

Q2 a) Enjambment   b) Caesura   c) Enjambment

Q3 a) Regular   b) Irregular

Q4 a) The waving man was loud and grimacing. *OR* The grimacing man was loud and waving.

  b) The poor lady was well-dressed but old. *OR* The well-dressed lady was old but poor.

Q5 **This question's open-ended, but here's a sample answer.** *Don't copy — write your own.*

  a) Glenda knew to go when the light went green.

  b) Glenda knew it was time to go when the traffic light turned from amber, eventually to green, with cars crawling reluctantly behind her.

  c) Glenda knew to glide away as the lights ticked and turned from amber to green, and the engines behind began to purr.

Q6 **This question's open-ended, but here's a sample answer.** *Don't copy — write your own.*

  a) The seething baker knew the flour had not even been bought.

  b) The jolly baker joked that the tasty flour had not been bought.

  c) The sweating baker trembled, and remembered the flour hadn't been bought.

Pages 16 – 17 — Comparing

Q1 b) The sea   Q2   a)

Q3 a) Keats's poem   b) Dickinson's poem   c) Both poems   d) Both poems

Q4 **This question's open-ended, but here's a sample answer.** *Don't copy — write your own.*

Keats uses powerful, onomatopoeic language such as "glut" and "swell" to describe the sounds of the "mighty" sea's rapid force inside the caverns. This is contrasted with the initial personified "whisperings" which convey the changeable temperament of the sea. This other, gentler aspect of the sea is developed further in the next section. This helps to create the idea that the sea is both very powerful and soothing for its onlookers.

In the first two stanzas, Dickinson mixes domestic language, such as "basement" and "upper floor" with the fantasy of "mermaids" to create a mixed idea of the sea as both an ordinary house, but also the home of fantasy and excitement. The seafaring language of "frigates" and "hempen" conveys a similarly ordinary view of the sea, but creates a sharp contrast with the exciting, personified version of the sea we are given in the rest of the poem, who "made as He would eat me up" when the narrator is in direct contact with it.

Q5 **This question's open-ended, but here's a sample answer.** *Don't copy — write your own.*

a)	Irregular rhythm	vi)	Slows down the pace
b)	Regular rhythm	v)	Increases the pace
c)	Enjambment	ii)	Evokes fluidity of the sea
d)	Lots of short verses	iii)	Don't allow time to reflect
e)	Undivided sections	iv)	Convey a completed picture
f)	Alliteration	i)	Helps to move the 'story' along

Answers for Pages 17 to 20

Q6   *This question's open-ended, but here's a sample answer. Don't copy — write your own.*

The irregular rhythm of the Keats poem slows it down, and enables the poet to make good use of enjambment, which evokes the fluidity and rhythm of the sea, running on from one line to the next. The poem is divided into three sections by punctuation, which each tell us something different about the sea's qualities, but the sections are not separated. This conveys a completed and concise picture of the sea.

In contrast, Dickinson's poem is a narrative, made up of short, regular verses, which run along rather rapidly, and include alliteration such as "no Man moved Me." This serves to move the "story" of the poem along, as the tide catches up with the narrator, but also suggests that the all encompassing sea leaves the narrator little time to reflect, as Keats encourages in his poem.

Q7   *Answers to Q2 a), Q4 and Q6 put together!*

SECTION 3 — ARGUING AND ANALYSING
Page 18 — Making Your Argument Convincing

Q1   a)   i) Bad. This is confusing and bogged down in too many numbers.
        ii) Effective. It is brief and clear.
      b)   i) Effective. Very clear use of the words of an obvious expert.
        ii) Bad. Much too vague to be convincing.
      c)   i) Bad. Very generalised and not specific enough. Vague words like "good" don't help.
        ii) Effective. Gives solid, real life evidence and also makes it clear what is meant by a "good grade".

Q2   *This question's open-ended, but here's a sample answer. Don't copy — write your own.*
        No one can deny that people the world over respond to rewards. GCSE results would improve dramatically if students achieving several 'C' grades, or better, were given a cash payment. Showing pupils that there is an immediate reward for their efforts will help them benefit in the longer term from a good education.

Q3   *This question's open-ended, but here's a sample answer. Don't copy — write your own.*
        This scheme would be relatively inexpensive and would help everyone. Individual students would improve their results and gain a sense of pride in their achievement. Schools would be able to motivate students who might otherwise miss out on a 'C' or who get little encouragement from home. The whole of society would benefit from better qualified, higher achieving generations of school leavers.

Page 19 — Making Your Argument Convincing

Q1   *This question's open-ended, but here's a sample answer. Don't copy — write your own.*

It is a widely held opinion that sixteen-year-olds should be given the vote. People who oppose this idea may feel that they are protecting young people from the challenges of adulthood but teenagers at the moment feel they have to cope with all the problems without being given any responsibility.

Supporters of this idea point out that sixteen- and seventeen-year-olds are often just as responsible and involved in their communities as older teenagers. They also feel that feelings of voter apathy may begin when people who are essentially adult are denied the right to vote.

You only need to be 16 to get married — a really life changing decision and one that is meant to be for life. Why not then allow people to make the choice of which political party to support when they are only required to stick with the choice for five years? If 16 is old enough to fight for your country in the army, surely it is old enough to be allowed to choose your country's government.

Q2   *First paragraph*: courtesy to people who disagree

Second paragraph: rhetorical question, and use of 'we' to help readers identify with the writer's point of view

Third paragraph: asks a rhetorical question.

Fourth paragraph: points made in threes, and use of 'you' addressing the reader directly

Q3   *This question's open-ended, but here's a sample answer. Don't copy — write your own.*

Mr Jones may have had unfortunate experiences with teenagers but he cannot fairly conclude that all teenagers are the same. Surely, as a fair-minded individual, Mr Jones must acknowledge that no group in society should be judged and condemned on the behaviour of a few representatives.

We all know that some members of any given group or age range in society could give their fellows a bad name. Would we condemn all middle-aged people on the basis of the activities of a few criminals?

Most teenagers are hard-working, idealistic and responsible. The year on year improvements in GCSE results could not possibly happen if they were all lazy. Those exam results show a determined, ambitious and dedicated generation working hard to achieve its best.

Page 20 — Think About Your Readers

Q1   *This question's open-ended, but here's a sample answer. Don't copy — write your own.*
        As the people most closely involved with our students you will want to know how this project will help them. I am glad to be

Answers for Pages 20 to 22

able to say that it will be constructed so rapidly that all pupils presently in school will benefit from swimming lessons without a long, time-consuming journey to a public pool.

Here at school we all feel strongly that the generosity of those who contribute to the fund should be acknowledged and the Art Department has agreed to produce special tiles bearing the names of all donors that will be used to decorate the interior walls of the pool building. I hope that people will be proud of having their family's contribution recorded in this way.

I know that everyone is aware of the importance of all children learning to swim as a way of protecting them from future danger as well as a useful exercise. I also want to assure you that we are well aware of the hazards involved in having a pool in a school where not everyone is able to swim. Rest assured that all possible security measures will be in place to ensure that no child can gain access to the water except when supervised.

Q2 **This question's open-ended, but here's a sample answer.** *Don't copy — write your own.*

Readers? All members of the local community who read the paper

Worries and concerns? Whether the money will be well spent / Whether it will take money from other projects /Whether it will change the atmosphere in the library

Counter-arguments? It's too expensive/It's not necessary/It will ruin the library

Q3 **This question's open-ended, but here's a sample answer.** *Don't copy — write your own.*

Readers? People planning holidays in this country

Worries and concerns? Cost / Places of interest / Suitable accommodation / Appropriateness of the area to their holiday needs

Counter-arguments? Lots of different places might be just as good for their holiday

Q4 **Mark your own piece of writing by looking back at the notes you made for Q2 or Q3.**
Have you given enough thought to: readers; their worries and concerns; their counter-arguments?
Remember you should also:
Use facts carefully   Use quotations from experts   Use relevant, real-life examples   Write in magic threes
Write in a polite and un-aggressive way   Use 'we' to identify with your reader   Use rhetorical questions

Page 21 — Analysis Essays

Q1 a)   There are often real problems of misunderstanding between parents and teenage children.

b)   Confining wild animals in zoos is considered cruel and disgraceful by many people today.

c)   Attitudes vary greatly but older people are usually more disapproving than younger people of swearing in public.

Q2 **This question's open-ended, but here's a sample answer.** *Don't copy — write your own.*

a)   Canned laughter on TV comedy shows is widely considered to sound false and artificial.

b)   If school canteens were to serve breakfast it would help all pupils make a good start to their classroom work.

c)   Teenagers get upset by people who make superficial judgments about them based on their appearance.

Q3 **This question's open-ended, but here's a sample answer.** *Don't copy — write your own.*

I really can't stand the way people fall for stupid so-called reality TV shows like "Big Brother". If all the millions of people who watch "Big Brother" were really interested in other people they'd go out and actually spend some time with real people instead of watching fake, attention-seeking fools parade themselves on the TV. Anyone who watches "Big Brother" is a fool.

The fact that millions of people watch reality TV shows like "Big Brother" shows that many people feel they offer stimulation and entertainment. There is a minority of television viewers however, which finds these programmes less appealing and finds it hard to understand why people would rather watch and get to know people on television than interact with real people in the real world.

SECTION 4 — INFORM, EXPLAIN, DESCRIBE
Page 22 — Using Evidence

Q1 *Well-supported*: b) and d)

Q2 a)   matches (v): Boys are consistently outperformed by girls. For the fifth year in a row, their performance in all exams, across a majority of subjects, has been the weaker of the two genders.

b)   matches (iv): Slouching can also lead to problems later in life. 56% of all back-pain sufferers in their fifties, admit to having had poor posture as teenagers.

c)   matches (i): It was not just the final scoreline which indicated the better side. A quick glance at all the statistics, from amount of possession to the number of bookings — shows that United were struggling that day.

d)   matches (iii): Athens cut traffic volume with remarkable results. Almost overnight levels of carbon monoxide halved.

e)   matches (ii): Children are getting fatter. Not only have exercise levels dropped in the last twenty-five years, but 87% of 13-16 year olds put TV viewing or playing computer games amongst their top three hobbies.

Q3 *Evidence sticks to the point:*   a) and d)

Answers for Pages 23 to 24

Page 23 — Making it Clear

Q1
- introduction
- calling up a search engine
- choosing key words for search
- scanning through search results for relevant sites
- conclusion

Q2 a) While I am away, you need to feed the goldfish too. <u>You will find the fish food on the kitchen window sill.</u> Add three pinches of it to the water every morning and two every evening.

b) <u>First, peel your onion.</u> Halve it. Take each half in turn and slice finely from the top through to the bottom. Further chop the slices if finer pieces are required.

c) Select the correct programme on the washing machine and load the correct amount of detergent. Once you have sorted your clothes into whites and colours, load just one pile. <u>Start the wash and let it run to the end of the programme.</u> Then hang your clothes out to dry.

Q3 a) It is a journalist's job to <u>elicit</u> information.

b) The students need to <u>write back</u> their <u>files</u> to the <u>hard drive</u>.

c) <u>Sautée</u> the potatoes in butter just before serving.

d) Once the <u>undercoat</u> is dry, apply the <u>gloss</u> paint.

e) "The <u>full-back</u> is <u>nutmegged</u> there — a real treat."

Q4 *This question's open-ended, but here's a sample answer. Don't copy — write your own.*

a) It is a journalist's job to investigate and find out information.

b) The students need to make copies of their files on the computer.

c) Before serving, shallow-fry the potatoes in butter, stirring them all the time.

d) Once the first, preparatory coat of paint is on, apply the final, shiny coat of paint.

e) "The attacking player there has just slipped the ball between his opponent's legs — a real treat."

Q5 *This question's open-ended, but here's a sample answer. Don't copy — write your own.*

a) Scroll down and find the ring tone menu then change it to something less embarrassing.

b) To turn on the phone, don't press the big button in the middle. You need to press the button which says "OK".

c) If the little symbol on the screen only shows one or two bars it means you have only got a weak signal from the transmitter and you may find it difficult to hear people when you call them up. Try going near a window or going outside and finding a spot where you can see four or five bars on the screen.

Page 24 — Introductions and Conclusions

Q1 a) The opening sentence is a question addressed to the reader which makes it sound as though the piece of writing is going to be personally relevant.

b) The opening question and the phrase "we bet you never knew" suggest an air of mystery to intrigue the reader.

c) The opening sentence asks readers to take sides in the debate so they are drawn into the argument.

Q2 a) The conclusion helpfully recaps the main points.

b) The conclusion states an opinion summarising the writer's point of view.

c) The conclusion leaves the reader thinking about whether or not they should take action themselves.

Q3 *This question's open-ended, but here's a sample answer. Don't copy — write your own.*

a) Opinions vary and at present no one point of view seems strongest. It is something that the British will no doubt turn their minds to when the issue is more pressing.

b) Overall, it is clear that the arguments for keeping mobile phones in school far outweigh those against.

c) The fact that Churchill was voted out in the first election after the war ended, should be a warning to those considering a career in politics — don't expect any gratitude.

Q4 *This question's open-ended, but here's a sample answer. Don't copy — write your own.*

a) Introduction: It's a real puzzle. The Spanish national side has had some of the strongest talent for many years, but only recently has the team had any serious success. We ask — what's changed in the Spanish camp?

b) Conclusion: Everyone agrees that staggering numbers of young people are choosing to leave the island rather than work in the banana groves. If the banana industry collapses the economy will collapse. If all the young people leave the island the community will fall apart. Surely the solution is to develop alternative industries which will appeal to young people, and sustain the island's economy. The islanders need to start thinking seriously about alternatives — before it's too late.

c) Introduction: Crochet isn't boring and it isn't just for old people. Its image is changing rapidly. Young people are learning to make their own high-fashion garments. We asked four young crocheters what made them take up their needles.

Answers for Pages 25 to 27

SECTION 5 — ORIGINAL WRITING
Page 25 — Say What Happened

Q1 *Time*: b) — could also be a) and e)   *Circular*: e) and f)   *Quest*: a), c) and d)

Q2 **This question's open-ended, but here's a sample answer. *Don't copy — write your own.***

   a) Julian opened his eyes and yawned. Mid-yawn he gasped and started edging out of the hammock. There was a tarantula eyeing him from a branch just above his face.

   b) It had been drizzling all day without stopping, and Mary-Lou thought that if it went on any longer she would probably shoot all the hostages without waiting for the ransom money.

   c) Lisa smiled through her veil at her husband-(very soon)-to-be. She just loved the way his boils glistened on a hot, humid day.

Q3 a) Fritz was to have many names over the next few months, not that he or Lucy, his owner, knew anything about it, of course. <u>Lucy loved dancing and horses and her favourite colour was amber.</u> She also loved Fritz, her dear little dog.

   b) Cathy was sick of it all — the constant rain, the grey streets and the grey people. <u>She was in good health and had her ears pierced.</u> She needed an escape route. <u>Her mother had been a great fan of toffee.</u> She needed something to aim for in life and the stage was where she was headed.

   c) Mr. Stanley sighed as another lump of plaster fell from the wall. <u>They had painted the walls pink a few years ago.</u> He shook his head and wondered when they could escape this old wreck which his wife just happened to love.

Page 26 — Go Into Detail

Q1 a) matches (ii) — spurs,   b) matches (i) — top hat   c) matches (iv) — oilskins   d) matches (iii) — chalk

Q2 a) Frank was washing his car down the road.

   b) The chair was bright yellow and had four plump red cushions on it.

   c) It was quite warm and the evening sky was tinted with purple.

Q3 **This question's open-ended, but here's a sample answer. *Don't copy — write your own.***

   a) The fire destroyed the two-storey house within hours, filling the sky with bright orange sparks, and filling the street with a sour, choking smoke.

   b) It was the best pizza Digby had ever sunk his teeth into. The base was light and crispy and crunched as he took his first bite. Now he could feel the tomato sauce oozing around the golden melted cheese. As he crunched into a chilli a pleasant burning sensation spread through his mouth and brought tears to his eyes.

   c) Martin searched in the dark for the hammer and gasped in horror when something suddenly yelped. Cold shivers ran down his spine and his armpits prickled as he strained to see through the impenetrable blackness.

Q4 **This question's open-ended, but here's a sample answer. *Don't copy — write your own.***

   a) Richard stepped up to the penalty spot. You've got to do it this time, he told himself and gulped nervously as he went for the ball. He sighed inwardly and hung his head in shame as the ball flew wide.

   b) Karen felt a hand on her shoulder. I don't believe it, she thought as she turned and faced the security guard, I've forgotten to pay for these dresses.

   c) Above his head, the blade of the guillotine glinted in the sharp autumn air. At least it's sharp, he thought, as he knelt down on the platform.

Page 27 — Pace and Style

Q1 a) fast   b) slow   c) fast   d) slow   e) fast

Q2 a) *Works*: tree branches have the same pattern as upside-down lungs, and in winter they are black, just as cancerous lungs are.
   b) *Doesn't work*: "swept" describes one movement, "swim" a different one, and "at night" is not relevant to movement or fish.
   c) *Works*: the despairing gesture and facial expression to match are similar to how a conductor might look at times when being very energetic and waving his arms.
   d) *Doesn't work*: wood and kiwi fruit don't look anything alike.

Q3 **There are loads more words you could use for this. If you get stuck for ideas use a thesaurus.**
   a) raced, dashed, pelted...
   b) leapt, bounced, skipped...
   c) burst, exploded, stomped...
   d) tiptoed, crept, edged...

Q4 a) <u>Judith hated it when he got like this</u>, and threw herself on the sofa. Richard ignored her completely. *She would never understand how he felt. Never!*

   b) <u>The black knight knew the last of his strength would leave him soon.</u> *The white knight saw the axe raised above him. He had to move or he would die from the blow.* The black knight swung with all his might, yelling as he aimed for his sworn enemy. <u>This was his last chance for revenge.</u>

Answers for Pages 28 to 31

SECTION 6 — MEDIA AND NON-FICTION QUESTIONS
Page 28 — Reading the Question

Q1 *A dictionary will give more detail but these definitions are a good start.*

Compare: look at similarities and at differences between two or more things. You usually need to look at details as well as overall effect.

Explain: making something very clear, often by looking at the reasons behind it.

Discuss: considering something in detail in your writing.

Contrast: highlighting the differences between two or more things.

Select: choosing an appropriate item from several.

List: giving a series of examples, often without much comment.

Communicate: getting an idea across.

Convey: carrying an idea, communicating.

Q2 *Here's a sample answer based on a cereal packet. Don't copy — write your own..*

  a) Pick out three claims made by the cereal manufacturers intended to prove that Wheat Pops is a healthy choice.

  b) This text is aimed at two different groups of readers: children and their parents. What is it seeking to achieve with these two different groups?

  c) Pick out two facts and two opinions about Wheat Pops from the back of the packet.

  d) Find three examples of language used to persuade readers and comment on how effective each one is.

Q3 *Most marks*: d) (because you have to comment on three different things — in b) you only have to comment on two.

  Least marks: a) (because all you have to do is find and copy phrases from the text — you don't have to comment on them or interpret them.

Q4 *I'm not giving you a sample answer for this one. You won't remember it unless you think it up yourself.*

Page 29 — Reading the Text and Making Notes

Q1 and Q2 *The answers to these depend on the article you're using. For part e) in Q2 make sure you use your notes from parts a) - d) to give as full an answer as possible.*

Page 30 — Writing Your Answer

Q1   b) is better because it is impersonal and begins to answer the question using some precise evidence.

Q2   a) is better here because it would make the examiner confident that the question had been understood and would be answered in detail. It starts to make links between the language and layout of the letter and the effect it has. The wording of b) is too close to the wording of the question. It is also vague and doesn't focus on the task set.

Q3   *This question's open-ended, but here's a sample answer. Don't copy — write your own.*

The leaflet tries to make the museum sound convenient to visit by emphasising practical features that will make a visit easier for different kinds of visitor. The leaflet describes public transport options and parking facilities so visitors from further away will know how to get to the museum. The leaflet also mentions a playground and cafe which should appeal to parents of young children. Finally, the leaflet describes how you can phone ahead to reserve tickets without queuing, which should appeal to people with a limited amount of time.

Page 31 — Writing Your Answer

Q1   a) assertion: uses the word "possibly" to cover up for having no real evidence.

  b) evidence: it's a straightforward statement with no attempt at fudging the answer, so it's likely to be based on fact.

  c) evidence

  d) assertion: uses the word "allegedly" to cover up for having no real evidence.

  e) assertion: "popularly believed" shows there's no real evidence, just vague gut feeling.

  f) evidence

  g) assertion: "by all accounts" shows this statement is just reporting rumour.

  h) assertion: "supposedly" shows this statement is just reporting rumour.

Q2 *Answer depends on the articles you're looking at. Remember you don't <u>have</u> to say that one is better than the other — it's OK to just say that they're different. e.g. a children's guidebook to London will be very different from a newspaper article about holidays in London, but that doesn't mean one is worse than the other. Judge the success of each article against what it's aiming to do.*

Answers for Pages 32 to 34

Page 32 — Writing About The Format of a Media Text

Q1 *In general the piece aimed at an older, professional audience will use: more text; longer paragraphs and sentences; a denser layout; and specialist vocabulary. The item aimed at teenagers will use less text and more illustrations or diagrams — but not always, so pay attention to the texts in front of you.*

Q2 a) This font is very clean cut and makes the company look efficient, but is probably too modern for a funeral director.

    b) This font is similar to the font you see in comic strips, so it is too light-hearted for use by a funeral director.

    c) This font is very uneven — the letters look like they're dancing about. It's too light-hearted and informal for use by a funeral director.

    d) The font is informal and not particularly stylish. More importantly, it's much harder to read than the other fonts, so it's not useful for advertising, where you want people to pick up the important information quickly.

    e) This font is formal, clear and traditional looking. It gives the impression that the company is serious and reliable. It's probably the most suitable for "Finnegan's Funerals".

Q3 *This question's open-ended, but here's a sample answer. Don't copy — write your own.*

    The font is clear and easy to read. Colour is used to highlight the important instructions. The layout is similar on every page to give the book a cohesive feel. Mildly humorous graphics are used sparingly to make the book less tedious. *It's gorgeous.*

SECTION 7 — LANGUAGE
Page 33 — Standard English

Q1 Standard English = c), d), f)   Non-standard English = a), b), e)

Q2 a) If I had known that yesterday, I'd've never done it, <u>you know</u>?

    b) I was watching Big Brother, <u>right</u>, last night, <u>right</u>.

    c) I can't believe we lost — I was <u>gutted</u>!

    d) Fifteen minutes into the film, Nari <u>chucked up</u> everywhere.

    e) That'll be done in a <u>jiffy</u>, <u>sweet as a nut</u>.

    f) Jason - <u>laters</u>!

Q3 a) You know <u>those</u> pens of yours? Let me see them.

    b) That is the man <u>who</u> sold most records in 1960.

    c) Do you still get <u>those</u> headaches?

    d) Them? They're horrible! Try <u>those</u> other shoes on instead.

    e) It was the poster of Will Smith <u>which</u> fell off the wall.

    f) It was *my* sister <u>who</u> won the high jump on Sports' Day.

Q4 *This question's open-ended, but here's a sample answer. Don't copy — write your own.*

    a) Charlie was very angry when he heard all the rumours about Tilly.

    b) A man I didn't know approached me and asked me to take his photograph.

    c) *Measure For Measure* by Shakespeare explores ideas of justice.

    d) It's much better than watching television.

    e) I'm always telling you to be on time, aren't I?

Page 34 — Punctuation

Q1 a) **T**he bicycle swerved to avoid the woman**.** **I**t was too late**.** **T**hey collided**.**

    b) **M**argaret had lived by the sea all her life**.** **I**t was a shock when she moved to the city**.**

    c) **T**he park stretched away from the house**.** **I**ts rolling fields were pleasant to the eye**.**

    d) **I** have change for the meter**.** **Y**ou can take these fifty pence pieces**.**

    e) **M**y feet are aching**.** **L**et's stop and have a cup of tea**.**

    f) **D**on't worry if you see a lion**.** **T**hey have already eaten today**.**

Q2 Correct = a) Wrong = b), c), d), e), f)

    b) Turn left at the traffic lights**,** then right**,** then right again**,** and it's just on the left.

    c) I was late**,** as you might well imagine.

    d) Books**,** papers**,** photos**,** clothes and ornaments were thrown all over the floor.

Answers for Pages 34 to 36

e) Crithers McFosfate, legendary horror writer, died yesterday in his Californian home.

f) The horse, hearing a loud noise, took fright and bolted.

Q3 Colon = b), d), e)   Semi-colon = a), c)

Q4 *Informal and correct*: a), b), d)

Formal and incorrect:

c) The second time Macbeth meets the witches he is brave: braver than before.

e) The image of Mrs. Park takes up most of the article. This technique is used to show her level of importance within the company.

Page 35 — Apostrophes

Q1 a) the briefcase belonging to Mum

b) the progress of her pupil

c) the chances of Arsenal winning

d) the bones belonging to the skeleton

e) the satsuma belonging to Terry

f) the calculator belonging to Hannah

Q2 *Singular*: b) Henry Kissinger's f) mother's g) Colonel Hitchpankster's

Plural: a) children's c) mice's d) flowers' e) soldiers' f) friends' h) cows'

Q3 a) It's   b) correct   c) It's

d) it's   e) correct   f) its

Q4 a) did n**ot** b) should n**ot**   c) can **not** , they **would**

d) I **will**   e) You **are**, I **would**   f) we **are**

Q5 **Here's my list, there could be more:**
you'd, you'll, you've, you're, I'd, I've, I'll, I'm, they'd, they'll, they've, they're, she'd, she'll, she's, he'd, he'll, he's, we'd, we'll, we've, we're, it'd, it'll, it's, can't, shan't, won't, don't, couldn't, shouldn't, wouldn't, haven't, aren't, o'clock, that'd, that'll, that's, ones like "Dave's" as in "Dave's gone to the shops", "Dave's an idiot".

Q6 *Possession*: a) donkey's c) dad's f) boys'
Omission: b) wasn't d) he's e) they'll

Page 36 — Speech Marks

Q1 **This question's open-ended, but here's a sample answer.** *Don't copy — write your own.*

a) "It's the third time I have come last in the 100m this year," *sighed* David.

b) "I love mashed up bananas! They're great!" *enthused* Craig.

c) "Do I look stupid to you?" *seethed* Judy.

d) Fred *hissed*, "You have had your last chance, pal. It's payback time."

e) Keeley *snapped*, "Look after yourself. It's not *my* job, is it?"

Q2 a) Alex tore out of the room and shouted, "**G**et down! It's about to blow!"

b) "**H**old it right there, buster," yelled the cop.

c) Kate shrieked, "**T**hat's the worst photo of me I've *ever* seen!"

d) "**H**old the line, please," said Jade, "**I** need to write that down."

Q3 a) "What do you think you're doing**?**" he shouted.

b) She turned to him with tears in her eyes and said, "You know I can't."

c) She smiled and said, "This is the best pizza ever**.**"

d) The fireman asked, "Are there any more people in there**?**"

e) Mr. Brown turned to the hotel rep and cried, "This is the worst holiday I have ever had **!**"

Q4 a) "You don't need to do that yourself," said Emma.

b) "Scale the wall? Scale *that* castle wall?" scoffed the soldier. "You must be joking, sir."

c) The judge cleared his throat and announced, "You have been found guilty of the murder of your wife."

d) "The buried treasure is mine when we find it," snapped the captain. "Understand?"

e) "Is it all right if he comes to school?" asked Mary, pointing at her little lamb.

Answers for Pages 36 to 38

f) "The wettest weather will be in the west," smiled the weather girl.

g) "Select only the freshest ingredients for your larder," simpered the TV chef.

h) "If I pick the winner tonight, I'll share my winnings with you," said Dad.

i) "Fifteen hundred fans gathered in the centre of town to welcome the cup-winning team home," announced the news presenter.

j) Bob stuck his head out of the changing room and said, "Can you bring me a size smaller please, Dave?"

Page 37 — Negatives

Q1 Positive = b), d), f) (there are no negative words in these sentences)   Negative = a), c), e)

Q2 *This question's open-ended, but here's a sample answer. Don't copy — write your own.*

a) <u>Always</u> look on the <u>bright</u> side of life.

b) I <u>would </u>start a long car journey <u>by</u> checking tyre pressure first.

c) You know Delaney always tells <u>lies</u>.

d) <u>Is</u> that your house over there?

e) <u>The car parks were full</u> in town on Saturday.

Q3 *This question's open-ended, but here's a sample answer. Don't copy — write your own.*

a) Nobody <u>ever</u> went to my Alfred's grave.

b) None of my family <u>is</u> clever.

c) You shouldn't <u>ever</u> stick your wet fingers in electric plug holes.

d) None of his kids look <u>anything</u> like him.

e) Police! Nobody move.

f) I <u>would</u> never have done it if I'd known.

Q4 *This question's open-ended, but here's a sample answer. Don't copy — write your own.*

a) I have been on no holidays this year/ I haven't been on any holidays this year.

b) I didn't eat any biscuits yesterday./ I ate no biscuits yesterday.

c) No women perm their ears./ There aren't any women who perm their ears.

d) There weren't any traffic jams in town on Sunday./ There were no traffic jams in town on Sunday.

e) A man doesn't have to walk down any roads before he becomes grown up.

f) I have no teeth in my head./ I haven't got any teeth in my head.

Q5 *This question's open-ended, but here's a sample answer. Don't copy — write your own.*

a) I get no sleep at night.

b) My baby has got no money.

c) We didn't love each other at all.

d) Nobody misses you like I do.

e) I am not sleeping at all tonight.

f) Never say goodbye to me.

Page 38 — Writing Proper Sentences

Q1 a) I <u>will go</u> back to my friend's house tomorrow, because he wasn't in today.

b) My cousins <u>come</u> to visit every summer.

c) Every Wednesday next year, I <u>am going/ will go</u> to Creative Sequinning classes.

d) Here — I <u>know</u> you, don't I?

e) My brother <u>plays</u> in a one man band.

f) When I was young, I <u>was</u> the cleverest in my class.

Q2 *These questions are open-ended, but here are sample answers. Don't copy — write your own.*

a) Karen and her mum walked back the long way.

b) Hippos will drown if they can't hold their noses under water and starve if they don't eat enough.

c) The best way to catch a butterfly is when it is resting.

d) Nobody knows who killed Sandra Bigginbottom but the murderer can't be very far away.

e) Just after midnight Daveena heard a noise, though Roxy slept through it.

f) There is too much traffic on the streets, especially in the morning and the evening.

Answers for Pages 38 to 40

Q3 ***This question's open-ended, but here's a sample answer. Don't copy — write your own.***

<u>On</u> the second day, Clarence noticed that the itch on his neck had grown swollen and red. By the third day, Clarence looked in the mirror and saw that the swelling had increased to the size of a golf ball. <u>On day four</u>, the itching was unbearable and the lump was the same size as a bowling ball. <u>Five days on</u>, he had to hold his head to the left because the swelling was so huge he couldn't hold his head straight. By the last day of the week, Clarence realised that this itchy lump was no mere swelling. He realised it was no hideous allergic reaction to an insect bite. <u>To his horror he saw</u> that he was, in fact, growing a second head.

Q4   I thought it was a terrible shame that Scotland and Wales did not qualify at all but I am sure they will next time. I was sad that England got knocked out in the semi-final, though they just managed to beat Argentina in the quarter-final so there was a bit of consolation. I was pleased Ireland got beyond the second round too. Some people were sad that South Korea didn't make it to the final. It was a brilliant final. Brazil won. I have to say, though, that the first round is my favourite bit because there is football on telly three times a day and all the teams are full of hope and energy.

Page 39 — Varying Sentences

Q1 ***This question's open-ended, but here's a sample answer. Don't copy — write your own.***
- a)   I had a memorable birthday. I got loads of beautiful cards and Mum gave me a delightful bracelet. Then, I had an exciting party and we ate a delicious cake.
- b)   This is exactly the right time to move house. The market is completely full of people buying and selling and it's one hundred per cent certain you'll get a good price. A good idea? Definitely!
- c)   Look at these incredible trainers. I got them for a bargain price. They look brilliant on my feet and they are perfect for comfort. If you got a pair, they'd look amazing on you too.

Q2 a)   We went on a school trip last week. We travelled by coach to Dizzyland. When we got there, I rode on six rides. The best I tried was called 'The Demon'. Dominic went on it four times. By the time we returned home, we were calling him Demonic Dominic.
- b)   When I saw Rebecca I told her that Amarpreet had said that she wasn't my friend. Rebecca replied that she hadn't mentioned anything like that and she didn't know why Amarpreet had said that to me. I got angry and shouted that I didn't care what she said. Then she got upset and she muttered she didn't want to be my friend anyway.
- c)   I watched the TV last night. There was a football match on that I wanted to see. Afterwards, I went out and looked at my cat trying to catch a bird. It didn't manage. It just stared at it for ages.

Q3 a) horrible   matches iv) unappealing
- b) easy   matches v)   unchallenging
- c) stupid   matches i)   nonsensical
- d) boring   matches ii) uninteresting
- e) difficult   matches iii) complex

Q4 ***This question's open-ended, but here's a sample answer. Don't copy — write your own.***
- a) Mum tried to give me an unappealing mouldy sandwich for lunch.
- b) This maths homework's far too unchallenging for a genius like me.
- c) Don't just make up words, it's nonsensical.
- d) I don't like chess, I find it entirely uninteresting.
- e) Well, OK, chess isn't boring, it's just too complex for me to understand it.

Q5 ***This question's open-ended, but here's a sample answer. Don't copy — write your own.***
- a) The train departed five minutes late.
- b) Spain was quite an impoverished country until a few years ago.
- c) The magazine was packed with loads of fascinating insights about make-up.
- d) The midfield kept allowing the other team to penetrate and attack.
- e) Your ability to write distinctive sentences has improved dramatically since you commenced working on this page.

Page 40 — Varying Sentences

Q1 a) <u>Polly's hair</u>   <u>the sun.</u>
- b) <u>The bird's egg</u>   <u>a gobstopper.</u>
- c) <u>The oak tree's trunk</u>   <u>a bus.</u>
- d) <u>Her voice</u>   <u>a police car's siren.</u>
- e) <u>Rosie's eyes</u>   <u>twinkling stars.</u>

Answers for Pages 40 to 41

Q2   a)   the colour
      b)   the size and shape
      c)   the width
      d)   the volume
      e)   the sparkling light in them

Q3   *This question's open-ended, but here's a sample answer. Don't copy — write your own.*
      a)   The tower block was as tall as a cliff.
      b)   The stream was muddier than a ploughed field.
      c)   The football crowd was angrier than a swarm of bees.
      d)   Her smile was like two rows of broken piano keys.
      e)   His hairstyle was shorter than the grass at Wimbledon.

Q4   *This question's open-ended, but here's a sample answer. Don't copy — write your own.*
      a)   The bathwater was as cold as an iceberg.
          The cold coin was like a tiny iceberg in my hand.
      b)   The receptionist was as unfriendly as a snarling dog.
          The boss was so unfriendly: like a snarling dog, waiting for me to make a mistake.
      c)   Answering this question is almost as exciting as riding a roller coaster.
          He said, "Playing this computer game is really exciting, it's just like riding a roller coaster."
      d)   She smiled, showing teeth as big as gravestones.
          Her teeth were like two rows of gravestones.
      e)   Her hair was as smelly as mouldy straw.
          She had hair like mouldy straw.
      f)   As he crept past the sleeping wolf, he tried to be as quiet as mice in slippers.
          He could hear the rain but it was quiet, really quiet, like the sound of mice in slippers dancing the foxtrot on a velvet rug.
      g)   He heard a voice, as heavenly as an angel's.
          The sound of her voice was like an angel singing the most beautiful hymn you could imagine.
      h)   The path was as narrow as a strip of ribbon.
          The path snaked to and fro like a ribbon blown by the breeze.

Q5   *This question's open-ended, but here's a sample answer. Don't copy — write your own.*
      a)   Martha is as funny as a dog on iceskates.
      b)   The hill is as steep as a cliff.
      c)   The boy usually eats like a starving wolf.
      d)   The dog is as smelly as a bag of old socks.
      e)   The old man grumbles like a broken radio.
      f)   Briony is as good at Maths as pigs are good at oinking.
      g)   Yasmine is always as tired as a sloth on Sunday.
      h)   Ann talks like a phone that's always ringing.

Page 41 — Varying Sentences

Q1   Literal = b), c), g)   Metaphorical = a), d), e), f), h)

Q2   *This question's open-ended, but here are a few sample sentences. Don't copy — write your own.*

    The first time I saw her, she stole my heart.

    She called me into her office to pick my brain about how to solve the problem.

    The beans are so cheap they're giving them away.

    I tapped him on the shoulder, and he jumped out of his skin.

    Pete tried to lie to her, but she saw straight through him.

Q3   a)   She <u>sailed</u> across the room.
      b)   He was so angry! At half-time he <u>exploded</u> at them.
      c)   Her face <u>shone</u> in delight.
      d)   She <u>rattled</u> off the points in favour of the proposal.
      e)   She <u>sieved</u> through the application forms quickly.
      f)   The sergeant-major <u>towered</u> above the new recruit.

Answers for Pages 41 to 42

Q4 *This question's open-ended, but here's a sample answer.* *Don't copy — write your own.*

a) 'sailed' suggests walking serenely

b) 'exploded' suggests great noisy emotional outbreak without control

c) 'shone' suggests an inner light of happiness showing on her face

d) 'rattled' suggests an even and rapid list, showing she is confident and familiar with the arguments

e) 'sieved' suggests that some of the forms were being eliminated: allowed to pass through without being chosen.

f) 'towered' suggests the sergeant-major is taller and more powerful.

Q5 a) He thundered across the room.

b) He slimed across the room.

c) He limped across the room.

d) He leapt across the room.

e) He sloshed across the room.

f) He crashed across the room.

Q6 *This question's open-ended, but here are a few sample sentences.* *Don't copy — write your own.*

Nervously — He crept across the room.

Gracefully — He danced/floated across the room.

Slowly — He inched across the room.

Quietly — He tiptoed across the room.

Page 42 — Language Words

Q1 a) The gardener took the shears and trimmed the hedge every Tuesday throughout the summer.

b) Sian and Cati had been friends for six years and there was a strong sense of loyalty and trust between them.

c) Clearly, the Directors must decide whether Paterson has enough skill to keep his place in the team.

d) All the things for the picnic were spread out on a tartan rug on the grass.

e) To build the cathedral, from the first brick to the last piece of wooden carving, took one hundred and thirty-three years.

f) Tragically, four field mice and a slow worm were killed when the river burst its banks

Q2 a) The gardener took the shears and trimmed the hedge every Tuesday throughout the summer.

b) Sian and Cati had been friends for six years and there was a strong sense of loyalty and trust between them.

c) Clearly, the Directors must decide whether Paterson has enough skill to keep his place in the team.

d) All the things for the picnic were spread out on a tartan rug on the grass.

e) To build the cathedral, from the first brick to the last piece of wooden carving, took one hundred and thirty-three years.

f) Tragically, four field mice and a slow worm were killed when the river burst its banks.

Q3 *This question's open-ended, but here's a sample answer.* *Don't copy — write your own.*

a) There was a minute rip in his trousers.

b) Look at that odious little dog.

c) I read this book in four days it was so absorbing.

d) The maths test was bewildering.

e) She dyed her hair bright pink just to be ostentatious.

f) They ran up a colossal bill at the bar.

g) She bought a really attractive jumper in that shop.

h) When I broke my finger the pain was excruciating.

Q4 *This question's open-ended, but here's a sample answer.* *Don't copy — write your own.*

a) Rory walked *confidently* into the room.

b) Felicity opened her mouth and shrieked *hysterically*.

c) Arabella curtseyed *politely*.

d) Bruce pointed *angrily* at the crowd.

e) Quentin lay back in the hammock and sighed *contentedly*.

f) "How could you?" said Dilys *tearfully*.

g) "Why is it always me that has to wash the dishes?" asked Matt *unhelpfully*.

h) Chris was unaware that the bull was running *rapidly* at him and Owen.

Answers for Pages 43 to 44

Page 43 — Checking Practice

Q1 *This question's open-ended, but here's a sample answer. Don't copy — write your own.*
"Access Denied" is the fourth film by <u>filmstar</u> Jean-Pierre Den Bosch to <u>be released</u> in the new millennium. His fans won't be disappointed by this <u>pacy</u>, <u>big budget</u> <u>production</u>, but if you're looking for <u>intellectual stimulation</u>, you'll need to <u>look</u> elsewhere.

The story is simple. A computer programme <u>develops</u> its own intelligence and <u>attacks</u> its programmers. Before long it is controlling every computer in <u>America</u> and there's only one <u>man</u> <u>who is intelligent enough</u> to stop it. So you don't <u>have to be a genius</u> to <u>predict</u> the <u>ending</u>, but the effects and music are <u>high quality</u>. We gave it three <u>marks</u> out of five.

Q2 <u>I</u>n the last twelve years the state of the promenade has worsened to the point of near dereliction<u>.</u> <u>I</u>f you walk along on any day<u>,</u> you will see overflowing rubbish bins<u>,</u> litter<u>,</u> fast food wrappers and spat out chewing gum on the pavements<u>.</u> <u>H</u>ow long are we going to accept this before we begin to change it<u>?</u>

<u>I</u>t is my proposal that we<u>,</u> as proud residents of the town<u>,</u> begin to make a difference to our own environment<u>.</u> <u>I</u> say we all need to set an example<u>.</u> <u>I</u>f you see someone dropping litter<u>,</u> don't just shake your head in disgust and walk on<u>.</u> <u>S</u>top<u>.</u> pick up the rubbish<u>,</u> and put it in the nearest bin<u>.</u> <u>I</u>f you know the person<u>,</u> why not tell them that you are unhappy with their behaviour<u>?</u>

<u>I</u>t won't do any harm to take a more active approach to looking after our town<u>,</u> and it might just make things look a whole lot better<u>.</u>

Q3 The dry dust of the desert blew in through the open door<u>;</u> it had drifted across the terracotta tiles<u>;</u> long wisps of its sandy fingers reaching into the dark interior of Elianna's humble cottage.

<u>"</u> Mother.<u>"</u>

A pitifully weak voice wandered through the body of the house<u>:</u> a young voice, frightened and weary.

But the voice would keep on calling<u>;</u> it would get no response<u>...</u> Elianna had left that morning and had no intention ever to return to the child or the house where she had lived all her life. Her child<u>'</u>s fate was now out of her hands<u>:</u> Elianna<u>'</u>s decision was final.

Page 44 — Checking Practice

Q1 *This question's open-ended, but here's a sample answer. Don't copy — write your own.*
LOCAL GIRL NANCY POISED FOR GLORY
Nancy Tucker, from the village of West Utheringstood five miles outside Endville, came second at the East Crawlshire Draughts Trials on Sunday.
Nancy, 17, had everything to play for. The plucky teenager said she was very nervous as she sat down to play her first game, but Nancy thinks she was even more anxious for the final round.

The local gamester's Mum and Dad, Terry and Hilary, were both really pleased. "We're dead chuffed," said Terry. Nancy was pipped to the post by last year's champion who comes from Busyton, but she thinks she's proved to be good enough to be selected for the County team.

The team needs three new players and selections will be announced next Thursday. Nancy's Dad is confident that his daughter's done enough to get in. "I think she's shown she deserves to get picked this year," said Terry. "She certainly has," concurred Hilary. Nancy will go through to play for the county at the East of Britain trials in August if she's selected. At seventeen, Nancy Tucker clearly has it all to play for.

Q2 *This question's open-ended, but here's a sample answer. Don't copy — write your own.*

HAROLD: *(sitting heavily on the upturned bucket)* I didn't think things'd turn out like this.

SKIPPER: You shouldn't've hoped for nothing. Them that didn't fight had no idea what life were like for soldiers like us.

HAROLD: *(pushing back his cap and scratching at his scalp)* But I *did* hope, Skipper. I was hoping there'd be flags waving and people shouting, just like there was when we left, remember?

SKIPPER: *(clenching his teeth)* Course I remember. The train station was packed with people, them that was staying safe at home. Little wonder they was cheering.

HAROLD: You shouldn't say that, Skip. Don't be bitter about it.

SKIPPER: Why not? Why shouldn't I?

HAROLD: It were a long time ago. It were almost fifty year ago, Skip.

SKIPPER: *(muttering)* Well it still feels like it were yesterday to me.